A Note on *Natural Beauty* Secrets:

This is the book that upset beauty thinking in America. Deborah Rutledge's remedies seemed too simple. The ingredients were available in the lady's own kitchen, or could be picked up for pennies at the grocery or drug store. And her recipes really worked!

Miss Rutledge cleverly sorts the old-wives tales from the generations-old and proven beauty techniques, in a guide which is entertaining to read, wholly reliable, and essential to the woman who *cares.*

NATURAL BEAUTY SECRETS is one of the most important books on beauty care ever published in paperback.

And now these secrets can be yours!

Natural Beauty Secrets

Deborah Rutledge

Being a Primer for
the Enlightenment of
the Fair Sex,
consisting of historic Receipts
for the Enhancement of
their Natural Beauty,
prepared and used in
the Sanctuary of their Homes

AVON
PUBLISHERS OF
DISCUS • CAMELOT • BARD

AVON BOOKS
A division of
The Hearst Corporation
959 Eighth Avenue
New York, N. Y. 10019

First Avon Printing, May, 1967
Fifth Printing, July, 1971

Hairstyle for cover model by Tomo in the Corner.

Printed in the U.S.A.

Contents

Read This First

I'm not going to call this an introduction because lots of people just skip anything labeled Introduction or Preface or Preamble. I want this to be read. It tells you what the book is and what it isn't, how to use it, and why I wrote it.

Women all over the world are interested in improving their appearance. They always have been, and they always will be. There's no argument there. The trouble is that they're willing to try just about anything if they can be made to believe it will add to their beauty.

The Ubangi belle slits her lips and inserts wooden disks to stretch them out into that exaggerated duck-bill look apparently so irresistible to Ubangi men.

In France it was once the style to wear dresses of the thinnest muslin, with no underclothes at all, and to put them on wet so that they would cling to the outlines of the body. Of course the women died like flies, of pneumonia, but they were mighty fetching while they lasted—a short life, but a popular one!

In my own era, I can remember the period after World War I, when the boyish figure was all the rage and the ideal feminine torso was the one that looked absolutely flat in front, even with a sweater. To achieve this, women bound their breasts with

7

heavy slipper satin, or other strong material, hooked on the side, from armpit to waist, as tightly as they could stand it and still breathe. Thus a whole generation of young women broke down their pectoral muscles and ruined their figures, all in the name of beauty.

These are among the more far-fetched examples of the varying standards of beauty, and this book is not about them. Nor is it concerned with those old-fashioned beauty remedies which today are impractical, save to repeat them as historical oddities for your amusement. I will not, for example, suggest that you bathe in ass's milk. No matter how beautiful it might make you, it's obviously not a practical idea today, and I'm sure your local dairy doesn't carry it.

But there *are* certain home beauty recipes which have been used over and over again for generations, in different countries and in different epochs, and the reason for their longevity is that they *work*. I have collected the best of them: from old beauty books, from dermatologists, from my own memory of what my mother and my grandmother and their friends have told me, and from women throughout this country and several others whose secrets have been handed down in their families from one generation to another.

Years ago, women couldn't cover up their defects with a variety of cosmetics. A "painted woman" was considered a bad woman, and even actresses didn't use make-up off the stage. Without foundation lotions and cosmetics, a woman simply had to have a good skin in order to be attractive. There were plenty of pretty women in the olden days. How did they do it? They did it by using home remedies, and if these hadn't been successful they wouldn't have kept on using them.

The big question that now arises is: Why should anyone today bother mixing up some messy goop at home when you can buy a nice pretty jar already made? There are two good reasons. One is that you can save a lot of money, and the other is that the home remedy is often a more effective one.

There is perhaps more hocus-pocus connected with the cosmetics industry than with almost any other. The advertisements tell us about the legions of white-robed scientists who, after years of bending over their retorts in secret laboratory research, have at last come up with *the* miracle cream. What they don't tell us about is the even greater legions of copy-writers with horn-rimmed glasses who are bending over their typewriters in advertising agencies, trying to think up words that will lure us into buying the cream.

Now I am as gullible as the next woman, if not more so. I have bought lotions for no other reason than that they were a lovely blue color or came in a beautiful pink bottle or had an entrancingly poetic name. Some of them probably helped my skin and some of them probably didn't.

I was among the first women to rush out and spend fifteen dollars for a tiny jar of cream containing jelly from queen bees, without once asking myself what a bee has that I would ever want. You can get it much cheaper now, but a recent medical article commented that there is no evidence that queen bee jelly has any appreciable effect on the skin. In other words, it doesn't hurt, but neither does it help.

The same article also tended to pooh-pooh the benefits of hormone creams on the basis that the amount of hormone extract used is so small as to be largely ineffective one way or another. That is the trouble with a lot of the commercial preparations. While they actually do contain whatever particular "miracle ingredient" is so extravagantly ballyhooed in their advertisements, the amount is too slight to be beneficial. A few years ago, the Food and Drug Administration Commissioner, George P. Larrick, stated: "There is extensive, big-time quackery in the cosmetics field, generally based on the exploitation of some 'miracle' ingredient that is supposed to re-

9

store youth and beauty to the unattractive or aging skin."

And in May, 1965, United States Senator Maurine B. Neuberger of Oregon told the Senate Commerce Committee that in her opinion American women are not getting their money's worth from the two and a half billion dollars they spend every year on beauty preparations. Senator Neuberger, who was co-sponsoring a "truth-in-packaging" bill to force cosmetic makers to list their ingredients on their labels, stated that two-thirds of the cost of beauty preparations goes into packaging, advertising and promotion, while "very little is spent on the beauty aids themselves." Thus, if she wants to, a woman can spend as much as $115 for a jar of cold cream (a well-known firm recently put a face cream on the market that sells for exactly that amount), but she cannot be sure how much of that sum represents the ingredients, how much pays for the advertisement that persuaded her to buy it, and how much is pure profit for the manufacturer.

There are on the market today creams with turtle oil, creams with extract of frog skin, creams with cow placenta (afterbirth), and creams with human placenta. Far be it from me to gainsay the salubrious effect of these rather unlikely-sounding unguents (and where do they *get* them?) but just what amount of them goes into the actual jar of cream that you rub on your face? An umpteenth of an ounce? Enough to do any good? The chief good goes to the firm that makes it, because even the tiniest fraction of an unusual ingredient gives it a great new selling point for advertisements. "At last! After twenty years of secret research, scientists have found the magic ingredient that makes women young again: powdered titmouse eggs!" You think I'm kidding? A new cream that came out in Europe last year contains caviar and trout eggs as a base, while another uses hormones from butterfly grubs (larvae). A French firm whose preparations are sold in America, too, manufactures one skin cream with extracts of chicken embryos—ugh!—and another one with "pure stallion serum." They are frightfully expensive.

That brings us back to the money question. Most women—and I have been one of them—are apt to think that if a beauty preparation costs an awful lot it must be good. There is no greater delusion; the mark-up in the cosmetics industry is enormous. A consumers' research magazine has pointed out that the ingredients in any cream or lotion actually cost only a few pennies, or sometimes even a fraction of a cent. What you and I pay for are often the old-fashioned recipes dressed up in fancy jars and given alluring names. Centuries ago, the Chinese used the ginseng plant for medicinal purposes. Today, a French cosmetics firm imports ginseng roots and uses their extract in a make-up base to "nourish the skin and improve the texture." It sells here in America for twenty dollars (plus tax) for eight-tenths of an ounce. Similarly, natural plankton (when I was a child, we called it "frogs' spit" when we saw it on the tops of ponds) was used ages ago as a healing agent, and it is now one of the "new miracle ingredients" in a costly beauty preparation.

I decided to do this book after almost a lifetime of falling for every expensive new "miracle cream" and "youth lotion" that was attractively presented in advertisements that caught my eye. I must have used creams with just about everything in them but the left ear of a newt or kidneys from virgin mice. I knew I was being a sucker for words. Although by law cosmetics manufacturers are no longer supposed to claim positive miracles, they can suggest them. Thus one cream was advertised in this way: "This is the cream that may well begin the age of agelessness for women." (Or, again, it may not. But you aren't supposed to think that. You're supposed to think that it *may*.) I am susceptible to this type of suggestion. So, apparently, are millions of other women, enough

11

of them to spend billions of dollars a year on the stuff.

I was talking about all this one afternoon with a well-known woman skin doctor. "I don't know why I spend so much money buying all these things," I said, "when I know from my own experience that there's nothing better for my skin than the simple things my grandmother used to use on hers." And I mentioned a few of the old home remedies. The dermatologist agreed with me unequivocally. "You ought to do a book about it sometime," she said. So here it is.

I am not posing as a medical expert, a professional beauty counselor, or anything like that. I am speaking only as a woman interested in my appearance, as all other women are interested in theirs; and I am not giving out any pseudo-scientific malarkey. I am writing in everyday terms and an informal style, as if I were actually talking to you face to face.

Some of the old-time beauty secrets I describe are used in modern, expensive, commercial products. Others have been forgotten for years and years, although their efficacy is bona fide. Naturally, I haven't used *all* of them myself. I have used a lot of them, though, or my mother has, or my grandmother, or various friends of mine who got them handed down from women in their own families. I know that every woman can find something here that will be genuinely helpful to her.

None of the practical hints which I specifically recommend should harm anyone, but there may be things that work with some women and not with others. There's no sense in being dogmatic about this sort of thing. I have no patience with those beauty advisers who say, "All women should wash their faces with soap and water every night!" or those who say, "No woman should ever use soap and water on her face!" You could go crazy trying to follow all the conflicting advice. The thing to do is to try what appeals to you, and what is easiest for you to do, and see how it works with *you*. If it seems to benefit your particular case, then stick to it. Give it a fair trial and make up your own mind. However, it should go without saying that if you have an allergy to any ingredient—lemons or glycerine, for example—you should be especially wary of using any recipe containing it.

I have taken care not to recommend specifically any recipe that includes an ingredient which, from my own knowledge and investigation, could be considered harmful under normal circumstances. I suggest, however, that a good general rule—to be followed by anyone who may have even a minor sensitivity to certain products—is to consult a licensed doctor for his advice as to any ingredients in a recipe about which you may have some doubt or about which you have no specific knowledge in relation to your own sensitivities.

This book can revolutionize your beauty care if you use it intelligently. You are supposed to pick from it what best suits your own individual needs. Don't, for heaven's sake, attempt to use *all* the remedies. When I was a child they used to advertise free samples in magazines, and I would clip the coupons and send for them and use them all, one after the other: treatments for dry skin, oily skin, blackheads, whiteheads, pimples, eczema, wrinkles. I had a perfectly good, clear skin, and it's a wonder I didn't ruin it, but I guess it was because I got bored with that in time and took to collecting pictures of movie stars instead.

If you like, you can use the beauty hints in this book as regular supplements to your favorite commercial products, or as special weekly or once-a-month tone-up treatments. Some of them you might adopt to clear up specific skin or hair problems, such as pimples, blackheads or dandruff. When you discover how helpful these old-time secrets really are, I think that you will use them more and more in your basic beauty care. You don't even have to bother mixing up different concoctions if you don't want to. There are plenty of simple, easy treatments here which I *know*, from personal experience, are amazingly effective. Even if you adopt only *one* of them, the book will have served its purpose.

But Is It Worth It?

We modern women are surrounded by outrageously glamorized versions of the ideal female. The movies, television, magazines and newspapers constantly hold before our eyes the images of incredibly beautiful young women, until it wouldn't be surprising if we suffered from the greatest mass inferiority complex in all history.

Gazing at these dazzling creatures, the temptation is to feel that it is impossible for us to approximate their standards—that we might just as well give up trying. Even the housewives in advertisements and television commercials are often portrayed as lovely sylphs, smartly dressed and exquisitely coiffed, made up and manicured. As they laughingly do their wash, merrily mop floors, and happily scrub sinks, their eyes sparkle, their teeth flash, and not a hair is out of place. Even when doing dishes, they gracefully flutter their beautiful, slim hands with almond-shaped nails in and out of the dishwater and joyously sing, "It sudses and sudses and *sudses!*" in liltingly seductive tones. We think of the picture we ourselves present when doing these same tasks, and our inevitable reaction is that it's all so far-fetched that there's no sense in bothering to fix ourselves up.

Well, it *is* far-fetched, of course, but the point we

don't realize is that none of these girls—movie stars or models or whatever—looked like that in the beginning. *They* bothered to fix themselves up. For one thing, almost none of them actually look as good in person as they do on the screen or in photographs. That's largely a matter of photographic angles, special lighting, and make-up. But, aside from that, they all had to do a lot of fussing around before they even began to look the way they now do in real life. If you look at early pictures of any of them—from Joan Crawford to Natalie Wood, from Marlene Dietrich to Suzy Parker—you will usually find it difficult to recognize them. Shortly after Marilyn Monroe's death, *Life* published a full-page photo of her at the age of nineteen. In that plump, frizzy-haired, toothy girl there was almost no resemblance to the world-famous sex symbol she later became.

I mention this just by way of proof that miracles *can* be achieved in personal appearance. But, you will say, these girls had, to begin with, basically good features and figures. That is true, but so have a lot of other girls, only they don't bother to make the most of them. There are very few of us who couldn't improve our looks if we really tried. Almost every woman has some potentially attractive features. Even plain or downright homely women can appear attractive if their complexions are radiant and their hair is shining. On the other hand, many basically pretty girls look awful because of bad skin. Sometimes it is just one flaw that ruins the whole effect, as, for example, an otherwise stunning girl with visible dandruff in her hair!

You may argue that the professional beauties were taken in hand by movie studios and made over by experts. Everything about them was restyled, including, in some cases, their noses, teeth, and figures. To a certain extent, this is true. But many of them still use their own home beauty secrets. This is above all true of the models, who can't afford high-priced beauty experts, especially when they're first starting out in their careers.

Furthermore, it is silly for the rest of us to give up and do nothing just because we can't afford expensive beauty care. That is where the old-time home treatments come in. The remedies recommended in this book are available to all of us. Any of us can afford them since most of the ingredients are in the kitchen or the medicine cabinet anyway.

I would suggest that as you read through the book you make a check mark in the margin beside the treatments you would like to try. Then after you see which ones seem to benefit you best, try to work out a regular system for using them.

I would advise you, especially at first, to list the treatments that you plan to do daily, as well as the ones you plan to do weekly or monthly. It will be a nuisance in the beginning, but if you stick to them, these treatments will become as much a part of your daily routine as brushing your teeth or doing your hair, and, in time, they won't take much longer. You should try to do them at the same hour every day, so that they become a habit. Set a special time, also, for your weekly or monthly treatments. You could apply your favorite facial mask and leave it on to do its job while you are reading the Sunday paper. Or if you are married and don't want your husband to see you (he'll love you just the same, but he may laugh at you), pick a day when you are doing the ironing or cleaning the house. That's one of the joys of the old-fashioned beauty remedies. You can use them at home at whatever time is most convenient for you. Not to mention all the money you save!

Is it worth the bother? Yes, it certainly is! The pursuit of beauty through the use of cosmetics is as old as history, and even older, for the instinct to improve her appearance is apparently inborn in every woman. Archaeologists unearth the beauty preparations of women of antiquity, and early chronicles record the oils and pomades with which our remote

17

ancestors sought to enhance their feminine charms. The methods may differ, but the aim has always been the same: to beautify themselves in order that they may appear more attractive in the eyes of men.

Even forgetting the male sex (as if we ever could!), there isn't a woman alive who doesn't feel better when she knows she's looking her best. To improve your appearance, even one aspect of your appearance—such as your hair, your skin, or your figure— does wonders for your morale. It give your whole spirit a lift, increases your confidence and poise, and even improves your relationships with other women, because if you feel you're looking better than usual it is easier for you to be charming and friendly. It often happens that women act irritable simply because they are conscious of the fact that their hair is a mess or their skin has broken out with blotches.

If you are lucky enough to be young and pretty and popular, then you should safeguard your looks by systematic care. If you don't fit into that category, then you're just plain crazy if you don't start right now to do whatever you can to improve the situation. *No woman is too young or too old, too beautiful or too homely, to be able to afford to neglect her appearance.*

3

Nature's Aids to Health and Beauty

There was a time, not long ago, when "old wives' remedies" were scoffed at by professionals and scorned by laymen. My own doctor, for example, sniffed at the idea of a mixture of honey, egg white and lemon juice as a remedy for coughs. Yet when my children were little and had bronchitis practically every winter, it was the only thing that stopped their coughing. I have also used it for myself, and friends to whom I have recommended it now swear by it.

By and large, there is a growing realization today that our ancestors knew what they were doing when they used nature's own ingredients in their remedies and treatments. Even doctors are beginning to admit what old-fashioned grandmothers have known right along: that inhaling the steam from a boiling teakettle is the best thing for the croup (the fact that today it is done by means of an electric vaporizer doesn't alter the principle); that warm camphorated oil rubbed into the chest and covered with a piece of wool flannel helps to ease a chest cold; that camomile tea is marvelous for dysentery or for nausea

19

(try it sometime for a hangover); and that many other simple, old-time treatments are astonishingly effective.

There is in medical use today a long list of drugs that have emerged from South American Indian lore, among them quinine, curare and the Rauwolfia drugs derived from Indian snakeroot. More and more scientists are digging into folklore medicine in different countries of the world, searching for curative ingredients that can be adapted for modern use. An Englishwoman recently spent ten months in the jungles of the upper Amazon in South America searching for drug plants known to tribal witch doctors in that area. She collected plants that are used to cure obesity, relieve hangovers, stop internal bleeding, heal burns, act as contraceptives, act as conceptives, preserve the teeth, and perform other medicinal functions. In other times, her discoveries might have been confined to an anthropological report on the "quaint" customs of superstitious and uncivilized native tribes. Today, her findings are being submitted to serious laboratory tests in order to determine how these age-old jungle secrets can be used to benefit modern man.

Similarly, we are rediscovering many old tried-and-true remedies in the cosmetics field. In 1961, at a symposium co-sponsored by the American Medical Association and the American Association for the Advancement of Science, Dr. Glen J. Sperandio, associate professor of pharmacy at Purdue University in Lafayette, Indiana, recommended natural foods as a primary source of the "very safest materials that might be used in cosmetics." Cosmetics can and should be "good enough to eat," he reported, and added that he and two assistants had produced a successful complexion lotion from peaches and cream, as well as an anti-chapping cream prepared mainly from tapioca. He further stated that certain fruits, vegetables, oils, creams, and other natural foods not only are danger-free cosmetics, but also have shown by tests to be as effective as the available commercial counterparts, or even, in some instances, more beneficial.

As a matter of fact, several modern cosmetic products do utilize foods, plants, and herbs. There are face creams and lotions containing lemons, cucumbers, eggs, strawberries, milk, and honey; and there are many egg shampoos on the market. A new bath oil blends French herbs, Spanish shrubs, North American evergreens, Mediterranean moss, bitter oranges from Paraguay, plants from India, and flowers. A skin-cleansing lotion mingles camomile, borage, Italian parsley, and water lilies. Another bath lotion turns out to be made of that old-time beauty bath favorite —regular whole milk.

All this is part of a definite new trend in beauty care: a renaissance of the old-fashioned cosmetics made of nature's own ingredients. A lengthy dispatch in the *New York Times* describes an elegant Italian pharmacy in Florence, founded in 1612 by monks of the Santa Maria Novella Convent. The pharmacy, which sells cosmetics made from the monks' formulas, is enjoying a sudden rebirth of popularity among chic women in Europe, including visiting Hollywood stars. Among the products are powdered iris root for the teeth, a hair-growing pomade made from new leaves gathered in the spring, and a facial preparation called "Virginal Milk," the recipe for which is given in Chapter 16.

A fashionable New York pharmacy recently had a window display of real cucumbers, an enormous green jar labeled "Pure Cucumber Juice," and stacks of cucumber cold cream jars and cucumber soap. Its owner also reports a sudden increase in the demand for whale oil soap, beer shampoo, and an English shampoo made with rum. Another pharmacy is boosting the use of camomile tea, sage, and cinchona bark in preparations for the hair, and almond meal treatments for the complexion.

Meanwhile, two skin-care salons in New York are featuring natural ingredients in their beauty treatments. One of them uses honey, eggs, oatmeal, and cucumbers in facials (a course of five facials for $125),

21

and the other stresses the use of herbs and oils. The proprietress of the second shop was quoted as saying, "It is funny, we have come back to the Egyptian way of treating the skin with natural oils and herbs."

Paris has gone all out for nature's own beauty ingredients. Two major salons there are using vegetables for everything involving skin care, for the body as well as the face. The famous magazine *Paris Match* reported on the back-to-nature trend of a new skin cream made of papaya fruit and another cream composed of fruit juice extracts, based on a secret beauty recipe of Sophia Loren. Other Parisian magazines advertise the efficacy of creams and face lotions with a base of oil derived from minks; and *Vogue* told its readers not long ago that "vegetable cosmetics are Big in France," adding, "We think the basic message of the fruit and vegetable idea will stand up for a long, long time."

None of this would have been news to our female ancestors. The old beauty books are crammed with nature's remedies for the care of the skin and the hair. Over and over again, women are advised to use the same treatments: the juice of melons, lemons, cucumbers, strawberries, and even green beans; eggs, honey, milk, cream, and buttermilk; oatmeal, almond meal, bran, and barley; cocoanut oil, olive oil, castor oil, almond oil; the fats from animals; and extracts from flowers, herbs, and other plants. Wine, whiskey, and brandy were often recommended for *external* use, and many a fair lady of olden times filched some of her husband's alcoholic beverages to use as a face lotion. In fact, a beauty treatment dating back to the women of ancient Gaul is to bathe the face with the foam of beer, fluffing it over the face and letting it dry, then rinsing it off with clear water after half an hour or so. This secret is still used by some women in Scandinavian countries. These women, who have fresh, glowing complexions, claim that the treatment acts as a tonic for the skin. This is not surprising when you consider that beer is brewed from malt, which, in turn, is made from grain, usually barley—and barley is one of the oldest beauty treatments for the skin.

This book will give you the recipes for many of these old-time treatments, and you'll see the same reliable ingredients popping up from one century to another. Take eggs, for example. Early Christians in ancient Rome used egg facial masks, and women have been using them ever since. Marie Antoinette and her court ladies used them; they were popular in Queen Victoria's time; and today they are still one of the best of the home treatments. An egg is an egg is an egg—to paraphrase Gertrude Stein. Eggs were the same two hundred years ago, or even two thousand. They were beneficial to skin and hair in olden times, and they are just as much so today.

Occasionally an old-fashioned treatment is given as a beauty hint in books or magazines or newspaper columns: put lemon juice on your elbows, rub avocado on your face, rinse your hair with vinegar. As a general rule, however, they have tended to be forgotten, except by the women who use them. This is the first book in modern times to collect them all together. Even many of the more outlandish treatments which I have included as historical oddities are not as foolish as they sound at first. In some of them, at least, there was a bona fide reason for their effectiveness, although they might be impractical for use today, either because of the difficulty of obtaining the ingredients or because they are too complicated and time-consuming. The treatments I have picked to recommend are still in use today by women in different parts of the world. Most of them are available to all of us—easy to prepare, easy to use, and costing only a few cents. These are the ones composed of nature's own ingredients. Our ancestors lived closer to nature than we do today; and they learned to make use of her own gifts as aids to health and beauty. Let's profit by their experience!

Pretty Ladies with Egg on Their Faces

The beauty mask—that is, some preparation you put on your face and leave on for a certain length of time —is the oldest facial treatment we know about, and its use antedates that of any of the cosmetics we know today.

In my early teens, a great favorite was made of fuller's earth, and it was marketed under several commercial brands, one of which was called Minerva, I think. It was a thick black cream that you spread on your face and which hardened like cement, making it absolutely impossible to smile or to talk. If you had it on and the doorbell rang, it was just too bad.

As far as I'm concerned, though, there is one mask that is the greatest beauty treatment of them all. This is the one I call the Wonder Mask. I suppose I really shouldn't give you my very best secret right off the bat. I should save it for somewhere later in the book, but I just can't wait to tell you about it, it's so great. My mother has used it for most of her adult life, and I am convinced that this is why she has today, at the age of seventy-six, the complexion of a woman of forty, or even younger. Doctors are always astounded at the youthful appearance of her skin, and truck drivers still whistle at her when she walks down the street. What better testimonial could you want?

I have used the Wonder Mask myself, always with excellent results, but I haven't stuck to it as faithfully as my mother has. This is because I'm often led astray by some glamorous-sounding new treatment that never turns out to be nearly as effective as the Wonder Mask. It's one of the oldest beauty treatments known to womankind, and it couldn't be simpler. Now that I've thought of it again, I am making a vow to use it at least once a week and stop horsing around with inferior preparations.

All you do is clean your face and then smear it with raw egg white. Leave it on for ten or fifteen minutes—or longer, if you want to—and then rinse it off with tepid water. You can feel it drawing impurities out of your skin, tightening it, and closing the pores. After you remove it, your skin is baby soft, looks clean and fresh and smooth, and feels wonderful.

When I use the Wonder Mask, I break the raw egg and slide the yolk from one half shell to the other, letting the white fall into a cup. Then I pat the white onto my face with a piece of absorbent cotton. (You can always save the yolk to put in scrambled eggs.)

If you try nothing else in this whole book, please try the Wonder Mask. I am positive you'll be delighted with the results, especially if you keep it up for any length of time. Experiment with leaving it on for different periods, from ten minutes to half an hour, and see which works best. If you can leave it on all night, it works wonders, but if you can't manage that, then do it for whatever length of time is convenient for you.

One great way to use it is as a pick-me-up for your face before going out on an important date, when you want to look your best. I used to use it this way when I came home after a day at the office looking like something the cat dragged in. I would leave it on my face for ten or fifteen minutes while I was busy doing something else, then rinse it off, and I looked like a new woman—rested, fresh, with even wrinkles and lines temporarily smoothed out. Even if I felt terrible, I looked fine!

Naturally, it is important to clean your face of all dirt and make-up before you apply this or any other mask. Although some authorities advocate very hot water followed by very cold (or by rubbing the face with a piece of ice), others claim that extremes of temperature are bad for delicate skin. I play it safe by using tepid water, sometimes followed by cool water. In warm weather, I use a pure, white soap, like Ivory, pure castile, Physicians and Surgeons, or Basis soap. Because my skin gets very dry in cold weather, I don't use soap and water then. Instead, I use olive oil, pure lanolin, glycerine, Johnson's baby oil, or Nivea skin oil.

I have found, in going over all my material for this book, that there seems to be a difference of opinion about glycerine. The majority of women I know who use it say that it whitens and softens their skin. However, there are a few who think that it makes their skin rough and red. I know that my grandmother always used a mixture of glycerine and rose water on her hands, and I, myself, have used this mixture, as well as the pure glycerine, on my face, neck, arms and hands. I like it; but apparently there are some women with whose skin it doesn't agree. They should only use it in mixtures or, if the allergy still persists, not at all. This is one of those things that are impossible to determine ahead of time. Lemon juice irritates the skin of some women, so much so that they can't use lemon soap. Others are allergic to different substances, like strawberries or cucumbers. Generally, however, all of these ingredients are beneficial in their effect.

Personally, I like Nivea skin oil better than anything else for cleansing the skin. Although a commercial product, it has been around for a long time, and its ingredients have been used in skin care for ages.

It was suggested to me by my dermatologist friend many years ago. You don't see it advertised a great deal, but you can buy it in drugstores and many department stores, and it's inexpensive. An actress friend of mine, who still has a lovely complexion although now in her fifties, has used it ever since she was sixteen, when her doctor father told her it was the best thing for her skin. I've never known anyone else in this country who uses it, although it's very popular in Europe. And I have heard that in recent years American models who have worked in Europe are using it and urging their friends to do so. (Nivea also makes a good, pure soap.)

If you do use soap and water to clean your face, pat it dry with a soft towel. If you use an oil, smooth it on and then wipe your face with facial tissue or absorbent cotton, being sure to get *all* the oil off—every smidgen! —and your face perfectly clean and dry before applying the mask.

Perfectionists insist that you shouldn't use a wash cloth because of possible bacteria. They say that you should put the soap and water on your face with your hands and rinse it off the same way. I think that's carrying hygiene a little too far, but you can suit yourself.

All of the old-time beauty books also make a big to-do about rain water. Pure rain water is supposed to be wonderful for the complexion (for the hair, too) but how are you going to get it? Besides, in modern cities, even if you did set a bucket outside every time it rains, you'd get a lot of soot and dust along with your rain water.

Incidentally, many of the treatments advocated in this book are equally beneficial for men. After all, women are not the only ones to suffer from problems like large pores, blackheads, pimples, dandruff, falling hair, and so on. You can do your menfolk a big favor by calling their attention to some of the simpler treatments. You might even, for example, persuade your husband to let you give him the following egg facial:

Scrub his face carefully with a mild soap and warm water. Pat it dry. Beat the white of one raw egg until stiff, and then mix in one teaspoon of honey. Using your fingers, or a pad of absorbent cotton, smooth this mixture over his entire face. Leave it on for fifteen minutes. Rinse off with warm water and follow with cool water. Pat dry.

Despite his embarrassed protests, he will probably enjoy having you fuss over him this way. Besides, when he sees how improved his skin looks, he may even be inspired to start using this mask treatment regularly himself. Used once a week, it will do wonders for blackheads or skin blemishes, and will help to keep him from looking tired or old before his time. (When you come to the chapter on the care of the hair, you ought to try some of those treatments on him, too.)

White of egg was formerly used in some of the more complicated facial masks. Marie Antoinette and her court beauties used one made by beating the whites of four eggs, together with one grain of camphor and one grain of alum, until stiff. (Camphor and alum are famous old home remedies to clear up blemishes and shrink large pores. You can buy powdered alum in the drugstore. If you can't get powdered camphor, buy camphor ice and mash it with a mortar and pestle or the bottom of a teaspoon.) Fluff this mixture all over the face and leave on for an hour or so, or even overnight. Marie Antoinette and her ladies-in-waiting also spread it on their necks and arms. In fact, all the masks and other face treatments should always be used on the neck as well, so that you don't have a clear, clean face and then, suddenly, a neck that is less than a complement to it.

Another egg mask, which is said to be thousands of years old, is made by combining three ounces of ground barley, one ounce of honey, and enough egg white to make a thick paste. However, I prefer to string along with my simple mask of just the plain raw egg white.

Most of the face masks, pastes, and creams are to be used at night and removed in the morning, but if you don't like sleeping in the stuff, there's certainly no law that says they only work at night. Personally, I'm opposed to using them then because they not only get stains on the pillow cases but they also frighten your husband half out of his wits. I prefer to apply them in the daytime when I'm alone in the house and not expecting any callers.

In the next chapter I will go into some other types of facial masks, each of which has its own coterie of devoted adherents who boast of its effectiveness.

5

Don't Just Eat the Food — Wear It!

Everyone knows that vegetables are good for your inside. What everyone doesn't know is that they are also good for your outside. Not only vegetables, but other foods, like fruit, eggs, honey, oatmeal, and milk, are wonderful ingredients for facials.

Our grandmothers and great-grandmothers and great-great-grandmothers knew this. Many of their beauty secrets came from their own gardens and kitchens.

The best of the all-time favorite ingredients are:

> eggs
> honey
> milk, buttermilk, cream
> oatmeal, bran, almond meal
> lemons
> cucumbers
> rain water, rose water
> vinegar, wine

31

mutton tallow (lanolin)
olive oil, cocoanut oil, almond oil
castor oil, mineral oil
borax, alum
glycerine, camphor, benzoin, petroleum jelly

They'll appear in many of the beauty treatments in this book. They're inexpensive, easy to obtain—almost all of them are things every woman has in her home—and they have been used by women to improve their looks for hundreds of years. In fact, some of them have been used for thousands of years.

Let's take a look now at some of the facial masks made of these ingredients. No mask is meant to be used every day. It is a special treatment which you use when you feel your skin needs toning up, perhaps once a month, or perhaps once a week, depending on the condition of your skin.

A simple old favorite is oatmeal and honey, mixed in proportions to make it soft enough to spread on your face, but thick enough so it doesn't drip off. Leave it on for half an hour and wash it off with water. No one appears to agree on just how long you should leave a mask on your face, but it would seem to me that fifteen minutes would be the minimum time. Longer might be better with some of them. You are the best judge.

Just honey alone, smeared on the face, left for a while, and then washed off, is said to be excellent for the skin. Don't ask me how it works! It's supposed to have all the ingredients to make it the one perfect food, and I guess that in some way these help to nourish the outside of the skin as well. I don't have a scientific mind, and my attitude is strictly that of a layman. All I know is whether or not something works. I can't for the life of me tell you why or how.

When it comes to reliable stand-bys, good old oatmeal wins hands down—or face up, as the case may be. Just about everyone who has tried it thinks it's the greatest, except me. I like my egg white better.

But, as I said in the beginning, try what appeals to you, find out what seems to be best for your individual skin, and then stick to it.

An old beauty book containing recipes for facial masks has this to say: "The humblest meals afford the average woman reliable and inexpensive methods for preserving her good looks if she possesses the wish to make use of these lowly agents. Cornmeal and oatmeal retain heat for a great length of time. When mixed with very hot water and applied to the face and neck as poultices, they draw out impurities, and make very valuable bleaching masks, especially if lemon juice is added."

Oatmeal in beauty recipes is raw, not cooked, but it has to be moistened with some liquid. One mask which is highly recommended is made of oatmeal mixed with enough buttermilk to make a paste. Another way is to mash oatmeal together with grated cucumber so that the cucumber juice moistens it enough to make it adhere to the skin. Or, again, you can make a mask of just plain oatmeal dampened with water. Spread this paste on the face, let it dry, leave it on for fifteen minutes or half an hour, and rinse it off.

Another mask, especially good for large pores (more about them in the next chapter) but beneficial for almost any type of skin, is almond meal mixed with just enough water to make a paste that spreads easily. There is an old-fashioned commercial almond meal for the complexion that has been sold in drugstores for goodness only knows how long, and it's wonderful, not only as a mask, but for a thorough cleansing of the skin. Wet the face and neck with warm water, put some of the almond meal powder in your hands with enough water to make it creamy, and rub it on your skin with your finger tips. You can leave it on to dry and then rinse it off with cool water after ten or fifteen minutes; or you can use it just as you would a soap to clean your face and neck, rinsing it immediately. Used every day in this way, it helps to refine the skin and prevent blackheads.

A lot of famous women—actresses, models and society beauties—have used the special treatment that comes next. Many of them originally learned it from a well-known and very expensive skin specialist named Gloria Bristol, who first became successful in the late 1930s and early 1940s. Her main specialty was peeling skin, a process in which she removed the outer layer of skin with, I believe, some sort of a saline solution. It took days and was a pretty uncomfortable process, but it left her patients with a clear, baby-like skin underneath the one that was peeled away. Dozens of celebrities had this done, including several glamorous but pimply debutantes of the era and Princess Juliana (now Queen Juliana) of the Netherlands. This, of course, was no simple home treatment but a complicated affair which had to be done by Miss Bristol herself, or at least supervised by her. However, if your skin wasn't bad enough to warrant taking it off, she advised a two-day home treatment for cleansing, stimulating and generally improving all types of complexions.

The first step, as in any treatment, is always to clean the face thoroughly. Scrub it, especially around the nose and chin, with a pure, non-alkaline soap, warm water, and a soft complexion brush, preferably one of badger hair. (That's what Miss Bristol said. Actually, of course, you could use your wash cloth or your hands. The point is to get the skin absolutely clean.)

The lather should be left on the face for five minutes, then removed with absorbent cotton pads which have been soaked in warm water and squeezed fairly dry. (Again, this is Miss Bristol's advice, but I don't see why you can't just rinse your face in the ordinary way.)

Following this, steam the face by covering the head with a large bath towel, holding it out with your hands

to make a sort of tent, and leaning over a basin of hot water. (Another good way to steam the face is to hold the towel in the same fashion and lean over the spout of a teakettle—beware of the "whistling" kind which forces the steam out under pressure—or a pan of water boiling on the stove. I first discovered how good steam is for the face when my infant daughter had the croup and the doctor told me to get one of those electric vaporizers and use it with water to which had been added a few drops of tincture of benzoin. Of course, I had to hold the baby in order to have her inhale the steam, so that both of us had our heads under the tent I rigged up with a sheet. Fifteen minutes to half an hour of this, four or five times a day for several days, not only cured the baby's croup but had a marvelous effect on my complexion!)

After the steaming, pat the face with a soft absorbent towel (speaking of babies, a diaper makes a perfectly wonderful face towel for these beauty treatments), and then rub beet juice on the face. You can use the juice from canned beets, if you want to, and leave it on for ten minutes. Then pat cotton pads soaked in lemon juice over the beet juice for another ten minutes. Finally, smear fresh cream, the kind you put in your coffee, over the whole conglomeration, leave it on a few minutes, and use it to clean everything off your face. Rinse with cool water.

The second day, scrub the face again with soap and water, and then steam it, this time with a lump of camphor ice in the boiling water. (You can buy camphor ice at the drugstore.) Following this, spread warmed honey on the face, leave it on for twenty minutes, and remove with water. Then put the lemon juice on, as you did the first day, and finally the cream again.

During the same era, a famous Hungarian dermatologist, Dr. Erno Laszlo, rose to prominence in America by advocating the use of natural food ingredients to cleanse and beautify the complexion. One of his special beauty masks was a paste of mashed cooked turnips and carrots spread on the face and left on for half an hour. He advised washing the face with milk at least once a day, and also washing it once a day with a blend of carrot and tomato juice. Oily skins, however, should be washed with cucumber juice, he said, and dry skins with a mixture of milk and melted butter. Dr. Laszlo is still head of the celebrated—and expensive—Erno Laszlo Cosmetic Institute in New York, and his clients have included some of the most beautiful women in the world, among them Greta Garbo.

Cucumber juice is an old favorite from way back and appears in many beauty recipes, one of the best of which is this:

> 3 ounces cucumber juice
> 3 ounces distilled witch hazel
> 1-1/2 ounces rose water

Rub into skin with the finger tips.

To make the cucumber juice, wash the cucumbers thoroughly and then cut them, with the skin on, into small pieces. Put in an earthenware or porcelain dish, pour enough hot water over them to cover, put over a low fire and let simmer for half an hour or more. Be careful not to scorch them. Then strain them through a colander.

Another way is to cut the cucumbers into very small pieces and mash them to a pulp. Then squeeze through cheese cloth or a sieve. This method gives you the pure fresh juice, or essence, of cucumber. (A blender is useful here.)

It would seem to me that you could leave out the rose water if you wanted to or if it might not be convenient to buy it. An old recipe for making it at home is this one:

1 pint oil of rose
20 grains carbonate of magnesium
8 drops warm distilled water

Mix the oil and the magnesium, add the water slowly, and filter. However, since you can buy these ingredients at a drugstore, you could probably buy the rose water itself just as easily.

To get back to cucumber, it appears over and over again in the old-time beauty recipes and is used as an ingredient in many modern creams. A hot-weather beauty trick of many fashion models is to rinse their faces with cool water in which they've mashed some cut-up cucumber. It has a very refreshing and beneficial effect.

As I mentioned earlier, modern professional cosmetics experts are continually digging up some old-time secret and incorporating it into a cream or lotion. Sometimes they don't pretend that it's a new idea but instead extol it as a sort of an archaeological coup. "Discovered! The secret of Cleopatra's fabulous allure!" This is always accompanied by a drawing of a ravishingly pretty girl attired in a burlesque stripteaser's version of an ancient Egyptian costume and bearing about as much resemblance to Cleopatra as Elizabeth Taylor does! (There are no portraits of Cleopatra which have come down to us, but all the available evidence seems to show that she had a prominent, aquiline nose, a very dark skin, a fat face, and slightly protruding teeth.)

Along this line, I was told of an incident which may or may not be true. According to the story, one of the cosmetics firms got all excited about the discovery of an ancient Egyptian beauty secret written on papyrus. Scholars had placed the date of the papyrus at around 2000 B.C. Among other recipes for the care of the body, it contained one which was a mixture of crocodile excrement, honey, soda, and some gummy substance. The efficacy of this was described in the papyrus in glowing terms. It was supposed to be the greatest ever and practically infallible. Fortunately, before the beauty company got around to figuring out ways and means of obtaining the necessary crocodile excrement, someone went back and took another look at the document. A more careful deciphering of the hieroglyphics revealed that the recipe was not a beauty preparation at all but a prescription for birth control!

6

Pimples and Other Problems

The previous chapter dealt with facial masks for general skin care. Most of them are also beneficial for treating pimples, blackheads, and large pores. But in this chapter you will find some other old-fashioned home remedies which were specifically recommended in olden times for these particular skin troubles.

For a serious condition, like acne or eczema, you should of course consult a dermatologist. An old-time remedy for eczema was to make a little cloth bag, fill it with pure bran—which you can buy at feed and grain stores—and put it in your bath water. This might be helpful in mild cases, but for anything persistent it's better to be on the safe side by seeing a doctor. The following home treatments are for the minor blemishes that afflict most women at some time in their lives.

PIMPLES
1. Mix equal parts of mutton tallow (pure lanolin), glycerine and castor oil. Melt over mild heat to blend, let cool, and keep in a glass jar. Apply to pimples until healed.

In most recipes where low heat is required, it is a good idea to use a double boiler. *Never* mix any of the beauty recipes in a metal utensil, unless it's one of those glazed, heavily enameled ironware cooking pots now imported from France, Belgium, Holland, or Denmark. Otherwise, use enamel, china, glass, or earthenware.

2. Here's another old-fashioned pimple cure, given to me by a woman who got it from her grandmother. Peel and cut up two or three onions. Cook them in lard until they are transparent. ⌐ ˟ cool, put between pieces of cheese cloth, and aℴℴℴly to pimples. Leave on as a poultice.

3. Brown or yellow laundry soap applied to pimples and left on will bring them to a head or sometimes even dry them up. This treatment is excellent. (It is also a well-known old-fashioned remedy for boils.)

4. Another old remedy that sounds all right, although I can't vouch for it from experience, is made as follows:

> 36 grains bicarbonate of soda
> 1 dram glycerine
> 1 ounce spermaceti ointment

Mix together into a smooth paste. Rub on pimples, let remain for fifteen minutes, and wipe off with a soft cloth, leaving a slight film still on the face.

As for the quantities involved in all the recipes, you can use the table of weights and measures in the back of the book, but it isn't necessary to go so far as to equip yourself with apothecary scales, measures, and so on. Perhaps, after discovering several recipes you plan to use regularly, you may want to buy a set of scales, but that is entirely up to you. If you don't know—and I certainly wouldn't—how much thirty-six grains is, ask your neighborhood druggist what would be the approximate equivalent in your kitchen measuring spoons. (Otherwise, I can just see you counting out thirty-six grains of bicarbonate of soda with a magnifying glass!) Usually, it doesn't make too much difference if you don't get it absolutely correct down to the last nth of an ounce. Use your own common sense, and since I'm not recommending any recipes with harmful ingredients, it won't matter if you put in a mite more or less than is specified. As a matter of fact, in the case of recipes like this one, you could have your druggist mix it for you, just as you have him mix a doctor's prescription.

5. The remedy for pimples that I like better than anything else is spirits of camphor, and I never go on a trip without taking some along. You can buy a small bottle at any drugstore. Keep patting it on the pimple every time you think of it, and if the pimple is just beginning it'll dry right up and disappear. If the pimple already has a head on it, apply a hot, hot cloth till the head practically pops out of its own accord, with only the gentlest squeezing. Then pat the camphor on it. It will sting a little bit, but it prevents infection and also makes the blotch heal rapidly. Spirits of camphor is great for insect bites, too.

BLACKHEADS

1. The best treatment for blackheads is to keep the face scrupulously clean. Steaming and scrubbing with soap and water are both good for these, as are any of the masks. The almond meal mentioned in Chapter 5 is especially recommended for this condition, or any of the oatmeal masks.

2. A meal wash specifically prescribed long ago for blackheads is:

> 16 ounces powdered oatmeal
> 8 ounces powdered almond meal
> 4 ounces powdered orris root
> 1 ounce powdered castile soap

Mix thoroughly. Slightly moisten about one tablespoonful with hot water to make a paste. Apply gently to skin with finger tips and rub into blackhead areas. Rinse with cold water.

3. An early nineteenth century care for blackheads on the sides of the nose was to rub them daily with lemon juice until they disappeared.

4. Another remedy, this one from the days following the American Civil War, was to rub them with a solution made of thirty-six grains of subcarbonate of soda dissolved in eight ounces of distilled water.

5. Still another old-fashioned remedy was to mix two ounces of liquid green soap with three ounces of witch hazel and use it on the blackheads with hot water and a complexion brush. This green liquid soap used to be highly recommended, not only for blackheads but for large pores as well. To make it at home, take equal parts of glycerine, water, alcohol, and green castile soap. Shave the soap into the water and stir over fire until the mixture is smooth. Add the glycerine and stir again. Remove the pot from the fire, add the alcohol, and stir.

6. One old-time remedy which sounds yummy is made by boiling two tablespoons of oatmeal (this is one time when you cook it instead of using it raw). When cold, add one dessert-spoon of white wine (Rhine wine, preferably) and the juice of one lemon. Pat it on the face before going to bed. If there's any left over, that solves your bedtime snack problem.

RED BLOTCHES

1. Cod-liver oil. You could use it plain, but there is a commercial ointment with a cod-liver oil base, called Desitin, usually sold for babies' diaper rash. I used it on my babies, and it was so wonderfully healing that the whole family now uses it on their own skins. It works like a charm on blotches, rashes, pimples, fever blisters, cold sores, or what have

you. Its effect is so magical that my husband always thought it would be a great idea for someone to make a commercial skin cosmetic with the same cod-liver oil base, but as far as I know no one has.

2. Boric acid. Dissolve in boiling water, let cool a little, and pat on the blotches while solution is warm.

3. Calamine lotion is also very good. Pat on and leave. (Also great for when the kids have chicken pox, as it not only heals but stops the itching.)

4. Dissolved borax in water, about an ounce to a pint. Dip absorbent cotton pads in the solution and keep applying to blotches.

LARGE PORES

1. The egg white Wonder Mask has a very beneficial effect on large pores, as does the paste of almond meal and water.

2. Buttermilk has an astringent effect on the skin and therefore helps to reduce oversized pores. This was a very popular old-time treatment, and I know several women today who recommend it. Pat it on your face with your hands or with absorbent cotton pads. Let it dry for ten minutes or so and then rinse off with cool water.

3. Mix equal parts of vinegar and hot water. When cool, use as a facial wash, patting it on with absorbent cotton pads. This has a tonic effect on the complexion as a whole, in addition to helping to refine the pores.

4. A few drops of spirits of camphor in cool rinsing water tightens pores and tones up the skin. One of the most famous beauty houses in London uses this on customers after giving them facials. It has been used by English women for centuries, and, as everyone knows, they are celebrated for their complexions.

There is also a camphor wash which was used in Europe long ago as a substitute for washing the face with water and which is very good for refining the texture of the skin. It is made of:

1/2 ounce glycerine
1/4 powdered borax
1/2 pint camphor water

5. A cornmeal and oatmeal mask is highly praised by some women. Mix equal quantities of cornmeal and oatmeal with enough hot water to make a paste. Pat on the face while the mixture is still hot. Leave on for about an hour (or all night if you wish), and then wash off with cool water. Following this, apply an astringent such as the above camphor wash, or put a few drops of spirits of camphor in plain cool water. You can splash it on your face with your hands or pat it on with absorbent cotton pads, whichever you like.

6. Powdered alum also used to be used as an astringent. One mask for large pores was a paste made by mixing powdered alum with raw egg white and rose water.

Some women advise putting a pinch of powdered alum in hot water—just enough to make a weak solution—and patting the mixture on the skin to tighten the pores.

7. Put slices of raw tomatoes on your face and leave them on for ten or fifteen minutes. Obviously you will have to lie down to do this. Spread old bath towels under your head and around your neck so if the tomatoes slip off they'll land on the towels. Actually, you should mash the tomatoes a bit, because it's the pulp that does the trick. Spread the pulp over the area where the large pores are—and pray the telephone doesn't ring just as you get all set.

Actually, while it may sound funny—and you may look odd while you're doing it—there is nothing really ridiculous about this treatment. Tomatoes contain certain minerals, vitamins, and acids that have an astringent effect on the skin. It's as simple as that. If these particular ingredients were isolated by a chemist, bottled attractively, given a fancy name, and sold at a high price, no one would think it was at all silly.

44

In fact, one of the cosmetics firms last year brought out what they advertised as a "sensational" new beauty cream made of tomatoes. The advertisement admitted that using tomato slices on the face is an old beauty secret and claimed that it is the amino acid that clears up the skin.

8. Here is a lotion for large pores that was used at the turn of the century. However, I do not know anyone who has actually tried it, so I cannot personally recommend it:

Put one ounce of cucumber juice in a half-pint bottle. Half fill the bottle with elderflower water and add two tablespoons of rose water. Shake well. Then add, very slowly, one-half ounce simple tincture of benzoin, shaking the mixture now and then. Fill the rest of the bottle with more elderflower water.

9. Roman ladies used to use poultices of bread and ass's milk for facial pores. (Apparently, women have always had the same skin problems.) I don't know if bread and cow's milk would do as well. However, regular milk baths, according to legend, are supposed to be good for the complexion. If you want to try plain milk, without the bread, heat it—but don't boil it; just get it warm—and then pat it into the skin wih absorbent cotton pads. Remove it with cold water after an hour or so.

10. A beauty book written in 1875 described large pores as making "the nose and cheeks look like a pincushion from which the pins have just been drawn" and suggested wearing a gauze or cotton mask dampened with distilled water. But the book warns that the mask must be worn every night for about six weeks in order to have the desired effect. (They never say how you can *breathe* with these cloths over your face all night, which is one reason I prefer to use any mask in the daytime.) I would be a little leery of this treatment, so I do not recommend it.

The same source also said that another good remedy is to rub the skin with milky juice squeezed from the broken stems of coarse garden lettuce. I don't remember ever seeing any lettuce with milky juice in it, but maybe they had a different kind in those days. I would be inclined to think so, since this lettuce was also supposed to have opium in it (said to be good for large pores if used externally—but no fair smoking any!) No wonder one of the old-fashioned hints for people who had trouble getting to sleep nights was to boil lettuce in water and then drink the water. "Good for nervous girls," the book says.

FRECKLES

People no longer worry about freckles the way they used to do. In olden times, freckles were considered an abomination, and any poor girl who had them would knock herself out frantically trying to get rid of them. Some of the remedies they used were dangerously extreme, such as applying various strong acids or rubbing the skin with coarse salt. (Probably took off not only freckles but some skin, too.)

Nowadays very few girls bother about this problem. A few freckles sprinkled on the nose can be quite piquant and attractive. Besides, you can always cover them up with a good make-up base. However, for those who might prefer to get rid of them, or at least fade them a little, the following remedies have been used at one time or another with varying degrees of success. Never having had any freckles myself, I cannot recommend them, except to say that those composed of lemon juice, buttermilk, or other ingredients previously mentioned in recommended recipes would almost certainly be harmless.

Naturally, none of these treatments is going to work any magic in just one trial. I imagine they should be used daily, unless your skin proves to be too sensitive, in which case try using them only once a week. If they still seem to irritate your skin, then discontinue using them and either try something else or give up entirely and reconcile yourself to having freckles.

1. Lemon juice. This is an old-time favorite for bleaching purposes. Pat on freckled area and let dry.

2. Buttermilk. Pat on and let dry, same as above.

3. Sour buttermilk. I don't know why this should be any more efficacious than the regular buttermilk, unless it's because there's more acid in it. *All* buttermilk tastes sour to me, so I wouldn't be able to tell the difference. One of the old-time beauty books, however, recommended the sour buttermilk as an application to fade freckles, although all the other old books advocated regular buttermilk.

4. Fresh green beans, boiled in water, mashed, and applied as a poultice.

5. Mix two parts lemon juice to one part Jamaica rum, and pat on freckles. (I suppose you can drink what's left over, and then you won't *care* whether you have freckles or not!)

6. One ounce of prepared horseradish you can buy at your grocery and one pint of buttermilk. Simmer together over slow fire for about an hour, stirring so it won't burn. Strain and then apply with absorbent cotton, but don't get it in your eyes. It's supposed to sting like everything. In fast, some of these remedies sound pretty strong to me, so if you do try them, use only a very small amount and be extremely cautious until you see how your skin reacts.

7. For light freckles, an old-time, harmless remedy is:

> 3 drams lemon juice
> 1 ounce hot water
> 2 drams borax
> 1 ounce red rose petals
> 1 ounce glycerine

Dissolve the borax in the lemon juice and the hot water. Put the rose petals in and leave them soaking for one hour. Then strain through cheese cloth. Let the clear liquid stand for twenty-four hours. Add the glycerine. Pat on freckles.

8. Another old-fashioned remedy, this one for persistent freckles, is to mix thirty grains of powdered borax with two and a half ounces of lemon juice. Apply at bedtime to freckles and leave on all night.

Finally, the freckle lotion to end all freckle lotions is one I found in a very old beauty book. I am certainly *not* recommending it, for obvious reasons, but it may amuse you to think of what some of our ancestors were willing to go through in order to get rid of a few freckles.

> 1/2 pound pure ox gall
> 1/2 dram camphor
> 1/2 dram burned alum
> 1/2 dram borax
> 2 ounces rock salt
> 2 ounces rock candy

Mix and shake well several times a day for three weeks, until the gall is transparent. Then strain it through a filtering paper. Apply to face during the day and wash off at night . . . Bye-bye freckles. Maybe bye-bye face, too.

SUNBURN

All of the following are good for sunburn and are harmless:

1. Vinegar. Take any commercial vinegar and pat it lavishly on the sunburned area. It takes the sting out and is very soothing.

2. Calamine lotion. Buy this in any drugstore, apply liberally, and let dry. It is really excellent.

3. Cut a fresh cucumber in small pieces and let the pieces soak for five or six hours in milk. Then pat the mixture on the burn.

4. A speedier remedy is to pat the face or other sunburned areas at once with half a cup of regular milk in which you have dissolved a pinch of baking soda.

5. Make a mixture of equal parts of lime water and linseed oil and apply to burn.

6. Cod-liver oil, or better yet the Desitin ointment (with cod-liver oil base) mentioned earlier, is soothing and healing for sunburn.

Here are some other old-fashioned treatments recommended by different women for various problems:

1. *For flabby skin.* Mix equal parts of milk and whiskey. Wash the face first with a pure soap, rinse it thoroughly, and pat dry with a soft towel. Apply the milk-and-whiskey mixture with an absorbent cotton pad. Pat it liberally on face and neck and leave on for several hours, or all night. Rinse off with tepid water. No lightning results are claimed for this, but I was told that if the treatment is kept up for a year, used once a week, it will result in a firmer skin.

2. *For oily or greasy skin.* Bathe the face night and morning with wine: white Rhine wine for fair skin, red wine (like Medoc) for olive skin. Do this about once every two weeks.

Another treatment used by some women for oily skin is to bathe the face once every ten days or two weeks with the juice of fresh strawberries or fresh cucumbers. Several women advised mixing the juice with regular white petroleum jelly and then using that nightly, rubbing it into the skin as you would a cold cream. This treatment, of course, could just as well be used at home in the daytime, which would avoid staining your pillow cases. If you do use night masks, you should spread a soft old towel (or a diaper —soft, lint-free, and very absorbent) over your pillow to protect the bed linen.

3. *For dry skin.* Apply the juice of honeydew melon in the same way as the strawberry or cucumber juice. However, most women—and I am one of them—feel that rubbing the face with castor oil, olive oil, or one of the other recommended oils is the best treatment for a dry skin.

4. *For perspiration.* An old-fashioned recipe for checking perspiration is to mix equal parts of boric

acid and powdered starch. Mild and harmless. (An old-time depilatory is made of ants' eggs, but this one I certainly wouldn't recommend.)

5. *For stretch marks.* Pregnant women are usually advised by their doctors to oil the skin on their abdomens daily in order to prevent the ugly wrinkles that often follow childbirth. The best thing there is for this purpose is pure cocoanut oil. If your druggist doesn't have it in stock, he can order it for you. Recommended without reservation.

6. *For hangovers.* As long as there have been wine and spirits, people—and that includes women—have suffered the "morning after" effects. In addition to the camomile tea mentioned earlier, they used to eat fresh parsley. Both of these remedies are still gratefully used today by those who know about them. Another old-fashioned hangover cure is to eat several teaspoons of honey—every half hour or so until you feel better. And Cicero once wrote that the best cure for this disastrous feeling is to eat raw cabbage leaves.

7. *For hiccups.* An infallible cure for hiccups, as far as I'm concerned—and everyone I know who has tried it says the same—is the old-fashioned one of eating a slice of lemon with a few drops of Angostura bitters on it.

8. *For warts.* Two old-time cures for warts have been recommended. One is to rub castor oil thoroughly into the wart every night and every morning until it disappears.

The other is to do the same using the juice from the milkweed—a plant that grows wild and has a milky, sticky juice. My doctor would probably laugh himself silly if I told him the following story, but it is true. When I was a child, I had a wart on my thumb, and an old, old lady told me one summer to rub it every day with milkweed juice. As the plant grew wild in a field near our house, I followed her advice faithfully. The wart disappeared.

There's More to You Than a Face

Too many women only bother about their faces and forget the skin on the rest of their bodies. They make the same mistake with make-up. They use a liquid foundation on their faces, put powder over it, and forget to carry it onto their necks and ears. The result is a sharp demarcation line of color of which they are unaware but which is obvious to the onlooker.

It is equally bad to leave your neck out of your skin care treatments. Masks, creams, oils, lotions, and other preparations should be applied to the neck as well as to the face, so that you won't have a clear, smooth face and a coarse-skinned, withered, muddy-looking neck. There are some additional treatments specifically for the neck, shoulders and arms, and this chapter deals with them, as well as with special bath ingredients.

THE NECK

The way you hold your head has a lot to do with the appearance of your neck. Unless you get in the habit of holding your head high, chin up and slightly forward, your neck muscles will become flabby, and as you get older you'll have that droopy look under your chin which is such a dead giveaway of the years.

The best way to learn how to carry your head correctly is the old one of practicing walking around with a book on your head. Once you've mastered this, you can expand it into balancing the book while going up and down stairs, sitting in a chair and getting up again, and so on, until it becomes second nature to you to hold your head erect. In countries where women carry baskets and other loads on their heads, they walk as proudly and beautifully as queens. Many schools for training fashion models use this method today to teach correct carriage. Some women are so good at it they can even balance a glass of water on the head while moving around, but that's pretty good, and you needn't expect to be able to do it right off the bat.

It is bad for the posture and for the neck tissues to use a pillow while sleeping. You're supposed to lie perfectly flat, but this is hard to do if you've been used to snuggling cozily into a pillow all your life.

Here are some special exercises for the neck:

1. Breathe slowly and deeply. Slowly bring the head forward until the chin rests on the chest. Pause a moment in this position, then slowly raise the head and drop it backward until it rests on the nape of the neck. Repeat these forward and backward movements five times each way to start, increasing to ten times or more later on.

2. Next, without moving the shoulders, bend the head toward the right shoulder, forcing it down as close to the shoulder as you can. (Don't cheat by raising your shoulder to touch your head.) You aren't expected actually to touch the shoulder, and don't strain your muscles. Do it easily and slowly. Raise the head and repeat toward the left shoulder. Do

this five times for each side, increasing the number gradually.

3. Rest a few moments and breathe deeply. Twist the head on the neck as if trying to look over your right shoulder at something. Repeat to the left, remembering not to turn the body or move the shoulders. Repeat five times each way.

4. The last exercise is to let your head go loose and swing it around in a circle. Don't worry—it won't drop off, and if you do it slowly enough you won't get dizzy. Describe a circle with the head five times in each direction.

In addition to the daily exercises, cream the neck and throat every night using upward, patting strokes. The following is a nourishing skin food, if you want to make your own:

    1-1/2 ounces almond oil
      1/2 ounce lanolin
      1/2 ounce spermaceti
      1/2 ounce witch hazel
      1/2 dram tincture of benzoin

You can have your druggist mix it up for you.

A lotion for whitening and softening the skin of the neck, as well as the shoulders and arms, is:

      3 drams powdered borax
    3/4 ounce glycerine
     12 ounces elderflower or rose water

Borax is one of the all-time favorite beauty ingredients. One old beauty book called it "as indispensable to your toilet table as soap or a nail brush." Just borax and water used to be used frequently to give a polished effect to face, neck, shoulders, and arms. Mix enough borax with water to make a saturate solution. Wet the skin with this morning and night, allowing it to remain on for several minutes, and then rinse off with plain water.

Another good old-fashioned treatment for coarse

skin on neck and arms is to rub them every night and every morning with the following mixture:

> 4 ounces refined linseed oil
> 8 ounces rose water
> 1/4 ounce tincture of benzoin

A simple-to-make neck cream that has been especially recommended to me by several women in England is made by mixing equal parts of lanolin and cocoa butter. You buy them at a drugstore and then beat them together over hot water in a double boiler, just softening them enough so that you can mix them smoothly together. Apply all over the neck, rubbing in well, leave on overnight, and wash the next morning with cold water.

SHOULDERS AND ARMS

Women used to pay more attention to their shoulders and arms than we do today. This was especially true of women who often wore ball gowns and wanted their shoulders to look white and gleaming. There were all sorts of recipes for achieving this look. One of them was to boil the whites of four eggs in rose water for just a jiffy, add one or two grains of alum, and beat all together. They spread this paste on shoulders and arms, covered it with old linen, and wore it overnight, or else all the afternoon before going to a party. It was said to give "great firmness and purity to the skin" and was also recommended for women with flabby flesh.

Here is another whitening recipe, also said to be good for chapped skin, which comes from the days of King James I:

> 1 ounce myrrh
> 4 ounces honey
> 2 ounces yellow wax
> 6 ounces rose water

Melt the wax, honey and rose water together in a dish over boiling water (we would use a double boiler today) and blend together by stirring. Remove from fire and add the myrrh while hot. After the mixture cools, rub thickly on the skin and leave on all night or for several hours before going to the party. It was advised for shoulders, arms, hands, and also for the face and neck.

My favorite, though, is an old Italian paste for the "face, bosom and arms." I've never tried it, but I think it sounds like such fun to make. Take equal parts of melon seeds, pumpkin seeds, gourd (squash) seeds and cucumber seeds. Grind them all to powder with a mortar and pestle, and then soften them with real cream, adding enough to dilute the powder. Next, thin the mixture with milk until it makes a paste of the right consistency for spreading, and, if you like, perfume it with three drops of oil of jasmine or a few drops of oil of lemon. Spread it on the skin, leave it on twenty or thirty minutes—or overnight, if convenient—and wash off with warm water. Ancient Italian beauties claimed it gave a "remarkable purity and brightness to the complexion."

ELBOWS

The most famous remedy for discolored elbows is to sit for half an hour with each elbow resting in half a lemon. If you feel too silly doing that, the next best thing is to beat up some egg whites with milk of magnesia and cover the elbows thickly. Wash off after several hours with lemon juice.

Some women recommend rubbing the elbows with coarse salt to get rid of rough skin. I think that probably the best treatment is to rub them daily (or nightly) with lanolin, castor oil, mineral oil, or any of the other oils mentioned frequently in these home beauty treatments.

Over and over again in the old-time treatments you will find the same things recommended for use in the bath for the purpose of improving the skin of the entire body.

The most common ingredients mentioned are bran and oatmeal. The bran bath, as a cosmetic for the skin, is prepared by stirring about a peck of common bran ("such as is used to stuff pin cushions," one source said!) into a tub of warm—not hot—water. Oatmeal is said to be even better because it contains a small amount of oil which is beneficial to the skin. These meal baths were especially recommended for dry skin. In addition to their cleansing value, they are said to give the skin feeling soft and velvety. After bathing, I think a shower would be advisable to remove all traces of the meal from the body.

More appealing to me is the idea of bath bags. Many French women still use bath bags of bran or oatmeal or almond meal, as taught them by their mothers and grandmothers. These bags are made from cheese cloth. Take a yard of cheese cloth and make it up into bags of whatever size is convenient. Fill with the bran or oatmeal or almond meal, sew up the fourth side, and let soak in the bath water a short time before you are ready to use the bath. Squeeze the bags several times, enough to let the meal penetrate the water.

Sometimes they make the bags large enough to use as wash cloths. Filled with the following mixture, they help to whiten and soften the skin of the entire body:

> 1 pound fine oatmeal
> 1/2 quart clean bran
> 2/5 pound powdered orris root
> 2/5 pound almond meal
> 1/4 pound powdered castile soap

If it's difficult to obtain the raw meal, you can use oatmeal flour.

Some of our ancestors advocated adding to the bath the water in which spinach has been cooked, but this doesn't sound very tempting to me. Another suggestion was to put three handfuls of fresh wild cowslip flowers into the tub and let soak in the water.

A more practical hint is to put a few teaspoons of glycerine or a couple of tablespoons of regular old-fashioned laundry starch into the bath water. Several women have told me that they have found that two big handfuls of Epsom salts in the tub have a very refreshing effect if they are feeling tired. An herb vinegar bath is also said to be fine for toning up the skin and refreshing the body. Take two drams each of rosemary, rue, lavender and camphor; soak in one pint of white wine vinegar for several hours; strain off the herbs and add the liquid to the bath water.

Obviously, we are much luckier today than were our great-grandmothers. In their time, a bath was quite a production. First, the water had to be heated in large utensils on the kitchen coal- or wood-burning stove. Then it had to be lugged into the bathroom and emptied into the tub. If the water got too cold while they were blissfully soaking in their cowslips or oatmeal or whatever, they couldn't adjust it by turning a hot water faucet. They had to hop out of the tub and run back to the kitchen stove for more hot water. It's a wonder they ever bothered at all, and as a matter of fact the commonest bath was the so-called sponge bath in which the ablutions were performed by dipping the wash cloth in a basin of water.

However, the therapeutic and cosmetic value of tub baths—apart from the question of cleanliness— has been known to mankind since the earliest days in history. There is something so soothing, relaxing, and beneficial about lying in a tub of warm water —especially one which has been made more luxurious by the addition of perfumes, oils, or skin softeners—that our ancestors were willing to go to all the necessary trouble of preparing it, and even, in the days of the Romans, of making it into a festive social event.

Men Always Notice Your Hands

Your hands are noticed almost as much as your face, and it's harder to hide imperfections because you don't wear make-up on them. Also, they are usually the first part of a woman's body to show the signs of age. Many women with young faces have wrinkled, old-looking hands.

Men always look at a girl's hands. There is something about soft, white, pretty hands that they find very appealing. Throughout the years they have rhapsodized over them in prose and poetry, comparing them to fluttering white doves and lilies, and trembled at their soft touch. "Pale hands I loved beside the Shalimar" and all that.

Your hands are always in evidence. You can't hide them. You can cover up your body, keep shoes on your feet, plaster your face with make-up, and wear a wig on your head—but you can't disguise your hands. Except for the short periods when you put on gloves, they are unavoidably on display.

There is nothing you can do about the shape of your hands or their size. But you can try to use them as gracefully as possible, and you can do something about their appearance. I will take it for granted that you keep them clean and use a lotion or cream or oil every time after you wash them to prevent roughness and dryness. Also that you don't bite your nails and that you manicure them regularly. I hope I am not assuming too much. Unfortunately, I have seen pretty girls, carefully made up and nicely dressed, whose appearance was spoiled for me by their slightly grubby little paws or their chipped nail polish.

The best way to have nice-looking hands is to use them as little as possible, but this is hardly a practical suggestion. Women who never do any work with their hands have far less trouble keeping them soft and smooth than the rest of us do. There is no doubt about it, housework does not improve the looks of your hands, and all the bleaches, detergents and scouring powders we use every day are murder on them, despite the advertisements to the contrary. I am getting pretty sick of watching models in television commercials airily flipping dishes in and out of foaming suds while cooing ecstatically how great they are for the hands. These women are picked for the job because they do have young and pretty hands, but they sure don't get them from scrubbing pots and pans, no matter what product they use!

Some women can do housework while wearing rubber gloves, and I guess that does help a little. I can't do it. There's an old Spanish proverb, "A cat with gloves on catches no mice"—and that's me trying to do dishes with gloves on. The only thing I can do is to keep rubbing creams and oils on my hands in a frantic effort to repair the damage done. I have found that what works best for me is the Nivea skin oil mentioned earlier in this book, or equal parts of glycerine and rose water. Pure lanolin (the wonderful old mutton tallow of our grandmothers' day) is also excellent and would be better for those women whose skins don't react well to glycerine.

Here is an old-fashioned recipe for keeping the hands soft and white:

> 1/2 pound oatmeal
> 1 quart warm water
> 1 tablespoon lemon juice
> 1 teaspoon olive oil
> 1 teaspoon rose water
> 1 teaspoon glycerine
> 1 teaspoon diluted ammonia

Soak the oatmeal overnight in the warm water. Strain and add to the liquid the other ingredients. Rub this into the hands at least three times a day and preferably more often.

Another old recipe is to boil a teacupful of oatmeal in about a gallon of water for an hour, strain, and use the liquid for bathing the hands night and morning.

Other remedies for redness and roughness include:

1. Rubbing the hands with camphor ice
2. Soaking them in a mixture of honey and orange juice
3. Massaging them with cocoa butter
4. Massaging with equal parts of cocoa butter, lanolin, and almond oil
5. Bathing them in a mixture of 3 ounces of lemon juice, 3 ounces of white wine vinegar, and ½ pint of brandy.

It goes without saying that whichever treatment you pick has to be repeated regularly in order to show results. You can't use any of them just once or twice and expect a presto-chango magic transformation.

The practice of rubbing some preparation on the hands and then wearing gloves to bed used to be a lot more common than it is today, although women still do it, and it's *said* to work better than anything else. One English woman told me that she used to know a woman who had the softest, whitest hands in the whole county, even though she did all her own housework. She attributed this to the fact that she went to bed every night wearing large cloth mittens filled with wet oatmeal. My informant neglected to mention how the woman's husband felt about this habit.

If your hands are in bad shape, you could try this glove business once a week, perhaps, as a special beautifying treatment. The thing to do is to buy cheap white cotton gloves, a few sizes too large. (One old beauty book advised "white kid gloves, the palms of which should be perforated with a stiletto"—using, I suppose, the stiletto you ordinarily wear stuck in your garter in case of attack by footpads or a jealous lover.) There are any number of recipes for the stuff to rub on your hands, so you don't have to stick with wet oatmeal unless you're crazy about the idea. Here are some that have been highly recommended:

1. Dissolve a grain of alum in raw white of egg.
2. 2 ounces white
   4 ounces oil of sweet almonds

Mix the wax and oil together by pounding in a mortar.

3. 2 ounces oil of sweet almonds
   2 ounces cocoa butter
   2 ounces white wax

Melt together in a glaze-lined earthenware pot over a low fire. Stir till cool.

4. 2 egg yolks
   2 teaspoons oil of sweet almonds
   1 ounce rose water
   26 drops tincture of benzoin

Beat together to make a paste.

5. 3 ounces lanolin
    1 ounce oil of sweet almonds
    2 drams glycerine
    2 drams rose water

Rub any of the above mixtures thoroughly into your hands at night, put on your over-size cotton gloves, and go happily off to bed, confident that when you wake up in the morning your hands are bound to be improved in appearance, especially if you keep up the treatment.

One old source advocates smearing the fingers thickly with carbolized petroleum jelly, wrapping absorbent cotton around them, and then putting on the gloves. This is for very rough hands or split nails. The petroleum jelly is supposed to be more nourishing for the nails than regular cold cream, and the carbolic acid is healing.

A modern remedy for nails that continually break or split is to drink gelatin powder dissolved in fruit juice. Knox Gelatin comes in boxes of small packets, each containing the proper amount to be dissolved in a small glass of fruit juice.

In olden times, honey and almond was a favorite combination for hand lotions, and Hinds' Honey and Almond Cream is an old commercial product that is still popular. Still another old formula, so old that we do not know its origin, except that it was very popular with court ladies in France during the reigns of Louis XIII, XIV, XV, and XVI, is:

the white of one raw egg
1 teaspoon of glycerine
1 ounce of honey
ground barley

Beat liquids with a fork. Mix in enough ground barley to form a paste. Rub into the hands at bedtime. Its adherents claim that it is remarkably beautifying to the skin of the hands.

To take stains off the hands or nails, rub them

with a slice of raw potato or a slice of lemon. If the stains are persistent, leave some lemon juice on for five or ten minutes. This will also remove nicotine stains from cigaret smoking.

Soaking the nails in warm olive oil is wonderful for them before a manicure. It softens and nourishes the cuticle. Also, if you can remember to do it, rub a little oil into the cuticle before you go to bed, or else massage petroleum jelly into it. If you have rough or ragged cuticle, this will do wonders for it.

Like most beauty care, these things involve a little extra time and trouble. However, in the end it is well worth it, especially in the case of your hands, which begin to look old and unattractive very quickly if you fail to take care of them.

And Don't Forget Your Feet

"Her feet beneath her petticoat
Like little mice stole in and out."

So wrote Sir John Suckling, the early seventeenth century English poet. Another English poet of the same period, Robert Herrick, wrote, "Her pretty feet, like snails, did creep . . ."

Today, few women's feet would be compared to mice or snails. Women's feet have been steadily getting larger, which is all the more reason why you should not neglect them. Not only is there more of them to be seen, but they are seen more often than they used to be. Of course, they are not as much in evidence as your hands, which is probably a good thing, because few people have pretty ones.

However, it's silly just to forget about them and then have to feel ashamed of them at the beach or at any of the times when they can be seen by other people. I have seen photographs of movie stars and models in bathing suits in which everything looks gorgeous except the feet, which in many cases are often very ugly.

What can be done to improve the appearance of

your feet? Obviously, the most important thing is to wear shoes that fit you. Corns and calluses are repulsive-looking, and they are caused by pressure from shoes. Much of this is unavoidable, fashions being what they are. Podiatrists are appalled at the damage women do to their feet by squeezing them into pointed-toe shoes, not to mention the high stiletto heels which tilt the foot at an unnatural angle and throw the whole body off balance, or the perfectly flat shoes which tend to break down the arches by failing to provide proper support.

There's nothing that can be done about this because all of us would rather be in style no matter what the physical cost. However, we can—and should—discard any shoes that are causing corns or, at the very least, cover the skin with a piece of moleskin at the point where the pressure is.

An old-fashioned remedy for corns was to take one ounce of fresh ivy leaves, put them in a pot or jar—something with a cover—and add enough vinegar to cover the leaves. Cover the pot and let the mixture stand for two weeks, adding more vinegar as it is absorbed by the leaves. At the end of that time, the leaves are ready to use. Put a leaf on the corn and bind it on with medical gauze. Keep changing the leaf until the corn is softened enough to lift out.

It isn't necessary today to go to this trouble (besides, you might pick poison ivy by mistake!) as there are plenty of ready-made remedies that can be bought at drugstores. The best thing is to go to a podiatrist, have the corns removed, and then take care not to wear the pair of shoes that caused them.

Calluses and rough spots can be kept under control by the following method: every time you take a bath, rub the calluses with a pumice stone—not too hard, of course—and after the bath, massage them with oil, glycerine, lanolin, or any good cream. Any of the oils and creams that are good for the hands are also beneficial for the feet, although you don't have to go so far as to sleep in socks filled with wet oatmeal! That *would* be grounds for divorce.

Rubbing the whole foot once a week or once a month with warm olive oil is an excellent beauty treatment. Massage the oil into the skin, especially around the nails and the calloused area.

For women bothered by excessive foot perspiration, powdered alum is the best thing and is still recommended today by doctors. In warm weather, it is a good idea, anyway, to rub powder on your feet before putting on stockings. If you don't wear stockings in the summertime, then by all means powder the bottoms of your feet or shake powder into your shoes. A good powder for this is made by mixing one ounce of powdered orris root, three ounces of oxide of zinc, and six ounces of any talcum. If your feet perspire, you could add some of the powdered alum.

For tired, aching feet, add the following to warm water and soak your feet in it:

1 ounce sodium sulphate
3 ounces bicarbonate of soda
4 ounces regular salt

There are many good exercises for strengthening the feet and relaxing them when tired. One of the best and simplest is to stand with your feet flat on the floor and curl your toes under. This forces your arches up and is excellent for strengthening them. Do it several times whenever your feet hurt or feel tired. It's really very good.

A regular exercise to strengthen the arches is to stand with feet flat on the floor and slowly rise as far as you can on tiptoe. Slowly lower the feet to the floor, and repeat. If you do this tippy-toe exercise ten times a day, to start, and gradually increase it, you will find that your feet become stronger and will not tire as easily. Afterward, if you have the time, massage oil or cream into the foot. If the feet are tired and aching, use the ball of your thumb to massage the area right at the base of each toe (on the top of the foot, not the bottom), using a rotating, circular movement.

Another trick for resting not only tired feet but also your whole tired body is to lie down with your feet up in such a way that they are higher than your head. You can do this, for example, by lying flat on a sofa and resting your feet up on the sofa back. If your sofa doesn't have a back, pile enough pillows under your feet so that they're on a line higher than your head. This is an oldie, from way back, and inspired the specially constructed "beauty boards" used—and sold—by some modern beauty salons. As with so many of their products, it's cheaper to do it by yourself at home, and just as effective, if not more so.

10

Your Crowning Glory — Mop or Mantle?

In the days when all women had long hair, the poets had a point in referring to woman's "crowning glory" or describing it as "a silken mantle." But the time has long since passed when girls boasted of being able to sit on their hair and when the celebrated Seven Sutherland Sisters toured the land displaying tresses which swept to their ankles. The only way a girl can sit on her hair today is if she sits on her false hair piece after she takes it off.

As for resembling a silken mantle, some of the hair styles that have been foisted on us in recent years have had more the appearance of a tangled old mop. The messy-Bessie hairdo initiated by Brigitte Bardot was probably the worst of these, although the poodle cut, the artichoke, and the beehive were runners-up. In my own childhood days, there was a hair-cut called the pineapple; the hair was cut in layers, each one a different length, and then each layer was curled upward. The result looked more like a Zulu warrior than a pineapple, but this style didn't last long, as it was too difficult to keep in shape. There was also, in the days of World War I, a ghastly arrangement of puffs made by teasing the hair—then called "ratting"—which was inelegantly known as the "cootie garage."

As a psychiatrist once wrote, "Man is so irresistibly attracted to woman that he will continue to love her, no matter how hideous she makes herself!" While there is undoubtedly a lot of truth in this statement, we should not interpret it to mean that we have carte blanche to ignore completely men's likes and dislikes. There is a difference beteen *fashions*—in hair styles as well as in clothes—and certain *basic tenets*. Men will tolerate silly fashions, but they will not tolerate messiness or lack of grooming. No matter in what style you wear your hair, it looks immeasurably better if it's healthy and shining. A weekly visit to a beauty parlor to have it trimmed, shampooed, and set is simply not enough to keep it in the pink of condition. The only way you can really keep your hair healthful is to work on it yourself at home.

Like all the rest of the home beauty treatments, this doesn't necessarily have to be a complicated job. There is nothing in the world better for your hair than the old, old treatment of brushing it. Brush it one hundred strokes a day and you don't have to worry about doing much else. No matter what's wrong with your hair, this usually will correct it. Shampoo it every couple of weeks, with a little vinegar or ammonia in the rinsing water; cut the split ends once a month; and you're all set.

However, there *are* other things you can do if you want to, and if your hair is dull or lifeless or thin, if it's too dry or too oily, or if you have dandruff, these additional treatments can speed up the correction of these defects. Here are some specific remedies, all of which can be used with good results even if there's nothing wrong with your hair, as they stimulate growth and help to keep the hair healthy.

70

1. Mix equal parts of vinegar and water. Part the hair and apply the liquid to the scalp with absorbent cotton. This is excellent for removing dandruff. It also cleans and stimulates the scalp. You can use it as a treatment by itself or before shampooing.

2. Beat one raw egg lightly with a fork and rub thoroughly into the scalp, using it instead of shampoo. Rinse out with warm water. Do this once a week.

3. Mix the yolk of one egg with one ounce of spirits of rosemary and one pint of warm water. Add a pinch of borax. Rub this thoroughly into the scalp. Wash it out with the following pure shampoo which is an old-fashioned recipe for completely cleansing the hair and scalp:

Cut one-half pound of imported pure castile soap in small pieces. Put in a porcelain pot with two quarts of warm water. Boil until the soap is dissolved. When cool, it should be the consistency of thin cream. If it's any thicker, add more water. Stir in one-quarter pint of ethyl alcohol. Let the mixture stand for several days in a warm room. Use a small quantity as a shampoo.

4. 48 grains resorcin
    1/4 ounce glycerine
    enough ethyl alcohol to fill a 2-ounce bottle

Shake before using, and apply every night to the scalp, rubbing it in well.

5. For persistent dandruff, try:

   1 ounce sesquicarbonate of ammonia
   1/2 pint spirits of rosemary
   1-1/2 pints rose water

Put in a bottle, shake thoroughly, and apply with absorbent cotton to the scalp, parting the hair. Then brush the hair.

71

1. Add one dessert spoon of ammonia and a pinch of borax to two quarts of warm water, and use this for rinsing water after a shampoo.

2. 1/2 pint ethyl alcohol
    1/2 pint warm water
    30 grains quinine

Rub into the scalp every other night.

3. Instead of shampooing, clean the hair every other week by shaking cornmeal into it and brushing it out. You can put the meal into a kitchen salt shaker. Spread newspapers on the floor to catch the meal as you brush it out. This treatment has been used for many, many years by one of the best known hair-care salons. The brushing of the meal through the hair removes the dirt and excess oil, stimulates the scalp, and leaves the hair clean, glossy and fluffy. Powdered orris root is sometimes used instead of the cornmeal, or mixed with it. (Incidentally, shaking cornmeal into furs and then brushing it out is also an excellent, safe, and inexpensive way to clean furs.)

4. Another treatment for oily hair calls for the use of the whites of two raw eggs. Beat the whites until very stiff and then apply to the scalp, using a toothbrush. Let dry. Then brush the hair thoroughly until you have brushed out every particle of the dried egg white. I prefer the corn meal treatment, but this one is recommended by several beauty editors today.

The best way to brush the hair is to lean the head forward and brush the hair from the roots outward. Use long, firm strokes, but don't brush hard enough to irritate or bruise the scalp. A brush made of medium-stiff, natural bristles is better than a nylon brush. Naturally, it should always be clean, especially if you have dandruff, because you can reinfect a clean scalp by neglecting to wash your brush and comb thoroughly. The best way to clean them is to put a little ammonia in tepid water and swish the brush and comb around in it until they are perfectly clean. Then rinse with cool water. If the comb is hard to clean, pour ammonia through the teeth and then soak the comb in the ammonia water for a while. After this, shake it in the water to release the dirt. (You can also use bicarbonate of soda or powdered borax in warm water instead of the ammonia.)

DRY, LIFELESS HAIR

1. Rub castor oil into the scalp at bedtime and shampoo in the morning. Do this twice a week at first and then once every two weeks. It puts life in the hair and makes it shining and healthy.

If you don't want to leave the oil on all night, rub the castor oil thoroughly into the scalp before you shampoo and steam it in by pressing hot wet towels on the head.

2. Massage warm olive oil into the scalp, steam with hot wet towels, and then shampoo.

FALLING HAIR

1. An old folk remedy for falling hair, highly recommended by several women, consists of alternating applications of castor oil and white iodine for four days.

On the first and third day, part the hair in small sections and apply white iodine to the scalp with a swab of absorbent cotton. On the alternate days, massage the scalp with castor oil in the same way. Don't use too much oil, as it makes a sticky mess if you do. Just put on enough to penetrate the scalp.

On the fourth day, use a little more of the oil and massage it well into the scalp. Then steam the head by wringing out a very hot towel and wrapping it around the head. Repeat the hot towel business about four times. Then shampoo the hair. One woman told me that this treatment stopped her hair from falling out after the first few days of treatment.

2. The juice of a lemon rubbed on the scalp is said to be good for preventing falling hair.

3.   1 teaspoon salt
    1-1/2 grams quinine
       1 pint brandy

Mix well and rub on the scalp each night.

4. Steep three onions in one quart of rum for twenty-four hours. Remove the onions and apply the liquid to the scalp. Use every other night at first and then once a week until the condition is remedied.

TO GROW HAIR

Anything that makes the hair healthy will contribute to its growth. Healthy hair grows normally, is neither too dry nor too oily, has no dandruff, and is shining and full of life. Therefore, any of the oil or egg treatments, the stimulating tonics, and, above all, the daily brushing, help to keep it in this healthy condition. However, in certain cases, these treatments have been found to be especially good for the purpose of encouraging growth of the hair:

1. Rub cocoanut oil on the scalp daily. (In Spain, many years ago, they discovered that the men who worked at cutting cocoanut palms, where the oil dripped constantly on their heads, had long thick healthy hair.)

2. Take several tablespoons of honey and thin it out by adding brandy, stirring them together. Massage into the scalp, leave on for several hours, and then shampoo out.

3. Stew one pound of rosemary in one quart of water for five to six hours. Strain and add one-half

pint of bay rum to the liquid. Rub some of this into the roots of the hair night and morning.

4.   5 fluid ounces tincture of cantharides
      5 fluid ounces Jamaica rum
      1 ounce glycerine
      4 drams sesquicarbonate of ammonia
     20 drops oil of rosemary

Mix together and stir into one pint of distilled water. Shake well and use as a daily massage for the scalp.

5. The following recipe for Macassar Oil was popular in the nineteenth century and was said to be one of the most powerful stimulants of hair growth ever known. However, I am not sure if it is possible to obtain all the ingredients today. You can try.

Take one-quarter ounce of clippings of alkanet root, tie in coarse muslin, and suspend in a jar of eight ounces of sweet oil for a week. Then add:

     60 drops tincture of cantharides
     10 drops oil of rose
     60 drops neroli
     60 drops lemon juice

Let stand, closely corked, for three weeks. Use as a massage lotion.

6. Rub kerosene on the head and leave on overnight. Shampoo thoroughly in the morning. It leaves no odor. I know a beautiful Cuban woman who has done this once or twice a month for years, and she has very black, long, thick, satiny hair, although she is now in her late fifties.

Here are some other hair tricks:

FOR BLONDES

1. Put lemon juice in the rinsing water after a shampoo.

2. Wash the hair in stale beer. (This is also good to use as a wave-set lotion.)

3. Mix one ounce salts of tartar with the juice of three lemons and one quart of water and apply to the hair and scalp before a shampoo.

FOR BRUNETTES

1. Put a little vinegar in the rinsing water after a shampoo. It makes the hair wonderfully soft and silky and has no odor.

2. My mother and my aunt both used to use Glover's Mange Cure years ago when I was a small child. Neither one of them had the mange, I hasten to add, but the treatment was supposed to make the hair healthy and thick. It was an awfully messy procedure, gooey and smelly, and it left dark stains on the towels they used. They used to rub the stuff into their hair and scalp, leave it for hours, and then shampoo it out. They both had beautiful black hair, and they were convinced it was due to this treatment, but I could never get up enough courage to try it.

FOR WHITE HAIR

A little ordinary laundry bluing in the rinse water after a shampoo makes white hair even whiter and takes away any of that yellowish tinge that white hair sometimes has. However be careful not to use too much or you'll wind up with baby blue hair. Experiment carefully to find out how much you need. I know several white-haired women who have used this trick for years, with excellent results. There is nothing worse than dingy white hair or yellowish white hair, but this bluing trick keeps it a beautiful, snowy white.

GENERAL HAIR TONE-UP

1. Beat six eggs (use Grade C eggs, as they're just as good for the hair as Grade A) with one jigger

of rum. Whip up a good foam and rub thoroughly into the scalp. Rinse and rinse and rinse with clear warm water. This is especially good for hair which has been bleached or dyed.

2. Mix one egg, one teaspoon of bicarbonate of soda, and one bottle of cheap red wine. Use as a tonic to massage the scalp.

3. Here is an old German recipe: Once every two weeks wash the hair with one quart of soft water in which a handful of bran has been boiled and a little white soap dissolved. Following the shampoo, rub a slightly beaten egg into the roots of the hair. Let it remain a few minutes, then wash out with warm water, rinsing well. Rub the hair dry with towels. Have ready a soft paste made of beef marrow boiled with a little almond oil or olive oil. Rub a small quantity into the scalp.

To make a good liquid shampoo, take a bar of pure castile soap (or any good white soap, although castile is the best for the hair) and cut off shavings with a knife. Add water to the soap shavings—enough to cover—and heat over a low fire until the soap is melted. The amount of water added depends on how thick you want the shampoo.

Some of these old-fashioned treatments are coming back into style in many of the big city hairdressing salons. Common food products now used by several New York hairdressers include lemon juice, milk, eggs, vinegar, olive oil, tea and stale beer.

There is an enthusiastic revival of the use of milk as a setting lotion. Those who advocate it claim that it adds body and luster to the hair, nourishes the scalp, leaves no flaky residue, and does not smell. The method of use is as follows:

First, shampoo the hair and rinse thoroughly.

Second, while the hair is still wet, spray on the milk, using an atomizer. Comb it through the hair.

Third, set the hair as you usually do with curlers or bobby pins.

If your hair is oily, you are advised to use powdered skim milk, diluted according to the package directions. If your hair is dry, use regular milk.

There is a difference of opinion among hairdressers as to the relative merits of milk and beer as a setting lotion. Those who are touting milk claim that beer has an odor, causes dryness, and leaves a flaky residue in the hair. On the other hand, the beer advocates vehemently deny all of this. I have never used either, since I don't wave my hair, but among my friends, stale beer is the favorite.

Generally, however, hairdressers agree on the beneficial qualities of the other food treatments, as follows:

Lemon juice is used as a mild bleach or to bring out natural highlights in the hair. It also helps to cut down oiliness.

Eggs, used in shampoos, give body and sheen to the hair.

Vinegar helps to make the hair soft and manageable, especially after the hair has been tinted.

Olive oil is an unbeatable conditioner for hair and scalp.

Camomile tea is one of the oldest known applications to bring out natural highlights in the hair.

The care of the hair has always been one of women's major beauty problems. Without her hair, the prettiest woman becomes a fright, as Apuleius wrote nineteen hundred years ago in ancient Carthage. Even the goddess of love and beauty, Venus herself, would be nothing without her hair, he said. "Take away the hair of a beautiful woman, strip her brow of this ornament, and had she even descended from heaven, were she engendered by the sea, begirt with her Cistus and perfumed with the most exquisite odors, if she appeared with a bald head, she cannot please."

He was, of course, dead right. After World War II in Europe, patriotic citizens shaved the heads of women who had been friendly with the enemy, choosing this as the most humiliating form of punishment, as even the most attractive girl looked terrible with no hair.

The women of ancient Egypt knew how to wave their hair and how to dye it. Cleopatra used bear's grease on hers, an expensive imported cosmetic in her country in those days. More than eighteen hundred years later in America, our great-grandmothers were still using it to improve the growth and luster of their own hair.

An interesting sidelight on hair, from a historical point of view, is that in ancient Greece and Rome dyed blonde hair was the official sign of the prostitute. During the time of Solon, in Greece, many Asiatic girls were bought as slaves and set up in brothels near Athens. They were forced to dye their hair saffron. They had no social or civil rights, and their children were excused from supporting them.

In Rome, too, yellow hair was the badge of the courtesan from time immemorial, until, eventually, certain fashionable Roman matrons (perhaps realizing how popular the others were) started dyeing their hair blonde, too, which must have been confusing to the menfolk, who no longer could tell which was which at first glance.

Aside from dyeing the hair, the chief preoccupation has been with treatments to make it grow and to prevent it from falling out. Whatever nourishes the roots of the hair obviously strengthens the hair. Beef marrow, one of the most nourishing substances known, has been used to rub into the scalp for centuries. Other oils used extensively in the nineteenth century were bear's grease, goose grease, skunk oil, fox grease, olive oil, oil of almonds (both sweet and bitter), fresh butter and burnt butter, and the oil of camomile nuts and of laurel. Nettle juice and the juice of white onions were also used to promote the growth of the hair.

These are all sensible, and their use is easy to understand, because animal and vegetable oils always have proved beneficial and doubtless always will be.

At first thought, the use of, say, skunk oil may *sound* silly to some of us today, but these animal oils were easy to obtain in olden times when people did their own hunting, and their efficacy was tested and proved.

It must be admitted, however, that some of the other old-time remedies do not sound as attractive, notably the use of bees—burned and then pounded to a paste in oil of roses—to make the hair grow. Yet, on second thought, when you come to consider even this treatment, it isn't really any odder than the use of queen bee jelly as a cosmetic. After all, the jelly has to be extracted from the bees in *some* way. The difference is that our enterprising female ancestors had to do it all by themselves at home.

The ashes of rats, moles, hedgehogs and other small animals were also used in hair preparations in the eighteenth and early nineteenth centuries. This sounds pretty disgusting to us today, but probably the animal oils in the ashes were beneficial in some way. The ashes were used to make soap.

During the early 1860s in America, a popular treatment to induce the growth of hair was to burn the roots of vines, turnips, and cabbages and to make lye from the ashes. Honey was massaged into the scalp and then washed out with a mixture of the lye and warm water. The treatment was performed for three successive days. I wouldn't recommend trying it!

A famous French recipe of the same era, which was said to have cured thousands of cases of baldness in men and to have increased the growth of hair in women, was made by steeping six ounces of boxwood shavings for two weeks in twelve ounces of proof spirit, mixed with two ounces of spirits of rosemary and one-half ounce of spirits of nutmeg. It was then strained and the liquid rubbed into the scalp every night and morning.

In ages past they used to have some pretty unusual ideas of how to improve the looks of the hair. Roman women used a concoction of steeped walnut shells to make their hair grow; Turkish women had their hair patted and stroked by slaves to increase its luster; the Chinese used a mixture of honey and flour; and early French women stewed nettles for a hair tonic. An old English beauty book advised against wearing starched nightcaps to bed—said the starch was bad for the hair—but admitted that it was okay to wear the nightcaps when "old age approaches."

In our own country, it was believed that you could dye the hair black in less than two weeks by washing it daily in spring water and then combing it in the sun, dipping the comb in oil of tartar, and repeating the combing three times a day. A complicated and slightly frightening recipe for turning the hair yellow was to make lye from the ashes of "vine twigs, briony, celandine roots, and turmeric" and then boil it with a mixture of "flowers of mullein, yellow stechas, broom, and St. John's wort."

They also used steel filings mixed with silver, nitric acid, and rain water to obtain a black dye— another mixture that sounds risky, to put it mildly. To thicken the hair, they dipped their combs in nettle juice and combed the hair the wrong way. And, of course, good old bear's grease was found in plenty of recipes for preventing baldness—sometimes mixed with port wine.

Fortunately, we don't have to resort today to any such drastic measures. Any of the simpler treatments given earlier in this chapter will benefit your hair, and above all don't omit the daily brushing. You will be amazed at what it does for you. Despite the recent popularity of wigs, there is nothing like having beautiful hair of your own. After all, there always comes a time when you have to take the wig off. Besides, they aren't very comfortable in the summertime. I can hardly stand my own hair on my head then, let alone wearing someone else's on *top* of mine!

11

Eyes Like Stars, Teeth Like Pearls

If the hair was the crowning glory to the poets of yore, the eyes were the windows of the soul and all that. This is not necessarily true. I have known women with beautiful, clear, innocent, shining eyes who were absolute little fiends. We are not concerned here though with a woman's inner personality, but with her outward appearance.

The eyes are probably the most important of a woman's physical attributes and usually the most attractive. In fact, when there isn't much else to say about a girl, you often hear the phrase, "Well, she has nice eyes."

Fortunately, today we are in a position to make the most of them. Eye make-up has not been as fashionable since the days of Cleopatra. There is no other cosmetic which can make as much difference in your looks, and the women of antiquity knew this. The ancient Egyptians used kohl to shadow their eyelids and outline their eyes in order to make them look larger and more mysterious. In Crete as long ago as 1500 B.C. women achieved the doe-eyed look by outlining their eyes with black and extending the black lines at the outer corners of the eyes, much as we do today.

For many decades modern women went without eye make-up, but now it's in style again, and it's so flattering to any woman's looks that I hope it never goes out of fashion. It makes ordinary eyes look attractive and beautiful ones even more so. I know a girl who has a dumpy figure, bad nose, buck teeth, and a skin scarred by acne. But she also has large blue-gray eyes with long black lashes. She uses blue eye shadow on the lids, black eye pencil to outline them and give the slanting, doe-eyed look, and lots of black mascara. The result is that her eyes are the first thing you notice about her, and you never get around to the rest. As one man remarked about her, "You know, that Jones girl girl hasn't got a thing except her eyes—but with them she doesn't need anything else!"

Aside from make-up, what can you do to improve the appearance of your eyes? Well, the best thing in the world is to get enough sleep. If you don't get enough, it shows right away in your eyes.

If your eyes are tired and you haven't the time to take a good nap, you can use an old trick of our great-grandmothers. They used to make weak tea, dip gauze pads in it, and lie down for ten or fifteen minutes—longer, if possible—with the pads on their eyes. The easiest way to do this treatment today is to steep tea bags for a few seconds and then cover the eyes with them when you lie down. This rests and brightens the eyes and is perfectly harmless.

An old-fashioned variation of this was to steep green tea in rose water, soak absorbent cotton pads in it, and use them the same way.

Two other methods are to use witch hazel to soak the cotton pads or a camphor wash made by putting a few drops of spirits of camphor in tepid water. Of the two, I prefer the witch hazel pads. They are both soothing and refreshing.

The simplest, most healing eye wash is an old one: pour a little boric acid into boiling water, let cool, and use with an eye cup. It is good for inflamed eyes, tired eyes, dust specks in the eyes, and many other eye irritations. In short, it's good for the eyes—harmless and painless.

An old recipe for eye wash advises mixing one teaspoonful of boric acid and fifteen drops of camphor in two-thirds of a cup of hot water. I am doubtful about the camphor. As long as the boric acid alone is so good, I see no need to bother with adding to it.

In olden times, Spanish women had a custom of squeezing orange juice in their eyes to make them look brilliant. I also found this recommended by women today in Switzerland—one drop in each eye before going out. As a person who can barely eat grapefruit without blinding myself, I certainly wouldn't ever try this orange juice bit or advise anyone else to do so, but apparently there are other women who think it's great.

Worse yet, one old recipe consists of eight ounces of rose water mixed with sixteen drops of lemon juice. I don't understand how a woman could even *see* to go out after bathing her eyes in this. Another helpful hint was to mix a few drops of vinegar in a tumblerful of rain water. Some women used to bathe their eyes with rose water in which rosemary had been steeped while others preferred plain white wine as an eye bath. I don't recommend, or even suggest, any of these.

An old beauty book also advised "flirting soapsuds in the eyes" to make them brilliant. Ouch! Still another said: "What girl does not know that eating lump sugar wet with cologne just before going out will make her eyes bright?" Well, this is one girl who didn't know it. I suppose it might possibly have been the effect of the alcohol in the cologne, but I wouldn't recommend it. As far as that goes, a few shots of liquor make your eyes bright, too, and it's a lot more fun.

As for the eyebrows and eyelashes, the best thing is to brush them daily with a small, rather stiff brush.

85

Rubbing cocoanut oil into them will help to promote growth, as will, to a somewhat lesser degree, castor oil. Lanolin, cocoa butter, almond oil, olive oil, and petroleum jelly all used to be used for this purpose—and still are—but I don't think they're quite as effective as the cocoanut and castor oils.

A very old recipe for stimulating the growth of the eyebrows consists of five grains of sulphate of quinine in one ounce of alcohol; but I wouldn't use it on the lashes, because of the eyes. Two other old-fashioned recipes for eyebrow tonic are these:

1. 3 drams tincture of cantharides
    1/2 ounce olive oil
    12 drops oil of nutmeg
    12 drops oil of rosemary

2. 5 drops sulphate of quinine
    1 ounce sweet almond oil

One woman's recipe for improving the looks of the eyebrows is to give them a sort of special shampoo once a week by rubbing a teaspoonful of well-beaten egg into the hair roots, leaving it on a few minutes, and then rinsing it off with warm water; afterward brush them into shape. This is perfectly harmless and serves to cleanse and nourish the eyebrow hair.

A safe eyebrow dye is sage tea with a few drops of alcohol added. Another harmless old dye is made by steeping walnut bark in cologne for a week, but it isn't always easy to lay your hands on a piece of walnut bark.

THE TEETH

The best way to take care of your teeth is to visit your dentist regularly and follow his advice. The old-fashioned remedies for care of the teeth are not necessary now that commercial preparations are relatively inexpensive. Here, however, are a few of them, not necessarily recommended, although they sound harmless:

1. Pulverize dried orange peels and mix with your regular dentifrice to whiten the teeth. This is an old Swiss treatment.

2. Wet the toothbrush and dip in a mixture of wood ashes and common salt. Back at the beginning of the nineteenth century, when everyone had a fireplace, this was said to be "perfect for brushing the teeth."

3. Use the ashes of burned bread—really *burned,* not just charred.

4. Burned rosemary ashes. (In olden days, rosemary was thought to have almost magic properties for just about everything—hair, skin, eyes, teeth—and maybe it has, for all I know.)

5. 1 ounce powdered myrrh
    a pinch of powdered green sage
    2 teaspoons of honey

This was a popular dentifrice around Civil War days.

6. 20 grams vegetable carbon powder
    10 grams carbonate of lime

Use as a dentifrice every three or four days. This is used by many Swiss women today, who learned it from their mothers and grandmothers.

7. Clean the teeth with a paste made of powdered charcoal and honey.

8. Crush strawberries on your toothbrush and brush the teeth with them to make them look white and polished. This sounds delicious!

The ancient Greeks made quite a culinary production out of mixing up toothpaste. Pliny originated a dentifrice composed of the ashes of hooves of oxen mixed with myrrh, burned eggshells, and powdered pumice. Of course, he was on the right track here, because modern dentists still use powdered pumice in cleaning teeth.

Hippocrates recommended cleaning the teeth with

a ball of wool that had been dipped in honey and then rinsing the mouth out with a mixture of dill, aniseed, myrrh, and white wine.

Pliny and Apollonius both advised an interesting cure for a toothache: "Scratch the gum with the tooth of a man who had suffered a violent death." Doesn't sound very practical.

One old-fashioned dentifrice that I *do* know is good and also harmless, because I've used it for years, is to mix salt and bicarbonate of soda in equal parts. It was recommended to me years ago by my dentist, who said it is an old-fashioned recipe and the best tooth powder he knows. Every once in a while I get sidetracked by some new commercial toothpaste, especially if it is expensive and foreign. I've tried toothpastes imported from Switzerland, Sweden, Italy, England and France. The French one is said to be made of ground sea shells, powdered seaweed and seawater, all allegedly good for whitening the teeth. But I always go back to the salt-and-soda mixture, or sometimes just plain bicarbonate of soda by itself, because I know that there's nothing better. I smoke a lot, and I have discovered that brushing my teeth with soda removes the brown nicotine stains. It also takes away the dark stains that can come from drinking a lot of tea—as I do—or eating foods which contain iron, like spinach and avocados. It will not remove tartar—that has to be done by a dentist—but it will help to *prevent* the formation of tartar. And it *will* keep the teeth white.

Finally, an excellent mouthwash can be made at home by adding rose water to plain water. Experiment to see how many drops of the rose water you need.

In the next couple of chapters we'll take up the problem which has always haunted women, and for which, alas, there is no permanent remedy. The traces, especially in the face, which prove that time does, indeed, march on, will probably always come. But if women can no more stop the advancing years than could old King Canute the waves, at least they don't have to wade out to meet them. There are a few tricks which will keep the signs of the times at a minimum.

❖ 12

You're Forty—
So What?

The worst thing about being a woman of forty is the way it sounds. This is probably why lots of women won't admit to it. You will notice that the majority of articles and books about Pooh-for-middle-age! and Life-begins-at-forty! are written by *men*. Women don't start saying they're forty until they're actually getting closer to fifty.

The reason that some women are not too eager to admit to being forty or over is that they are still mental slaves to an outworn prejudice: the tradition that the fortieth birthday is some sort of a demarcation line in a woman's life. On one side of the line she is considered still in the running; on the other, she is relegated to the shelf. Although it has little relation to the truth, the phrase "a woman of forty" often evokes a mental image of an ample-hipped, thick-waisted, motherly creature with graying hair, a double chin, and a passionate interest in putting up peach preserves. The result is that you find women who will go on being thirty-nine forever, rather than give voice to the awful truth. I even know a woman of ninety-two who says she is only eighty-seven, but that's carrying things a bit far!

I am considerably more than forty now, but I can well remember the first few months after my own fortieth birthday. I was so obsessed by the dire fate that had inexorably overtaken me that I never gave myself, or anyone else, a chance to forget it. I was all prepared to settle down in a rocking chair with my shawl, some felt carpet slippers, and a suitable hobby, such as tatting. I would peer at myself in the mirror, pulling out gray hairs with tweezers, but since I always managed to yank out four or five brown hairs before I finally got a firm grip on the white one I was after, I could see that this was no solution to my problem.

For months after my birthday I dragged references to my age into every conversation. "Imagine, at *my* age!" I would say, with a deprecating little laugh, or, "Listen, when you get to be *my* age. . . ." I wouldn't let anyone ignore the fact, but doggedly kept reminding them of it. I would keep referring to old songs, old customs, old events—even ones that were actually way before my time—and went around talking as if I were at least 110.

It was not that I was any vainer than anyone else. It was just that, for a woman, there seemed something so *final* about reaching forty. All the books, the magazine fiction, the newspaper stories referred to women of that age as "middle-aged." "She was a sweet-faced, middle-aged woman of forty." "She was an attractive, well-preserved woman of forty, with graying hair." "Middle-aged woman, forty, battered to death in hammer murder. . . ." I winced every time I saw the phrase in print.

I developed an abnormal interest in advertisements reading "Brown spots on your hands? Telltale marks of age?" and rediscovered with dismay my own brown spots, which as a matter of fact I had had since I was a child. There they were, indubitable proof of my dotage. I was a sucker for any advertisement which teed off with the query: "Over thirty-five?" I never went so far as to buy any of the products, because I figured I was so long over thirty-five that I was too far gone for aid.

One thing I did try once was a little petroleum jelly under the eyes, mentioned in a beauty article as giving you "a fresh, dewy, youthful look." My best friend took one glance at me and hissed, "For God's sake, powder your face." I explained to her that I was supposed to look dewy. "Dewy?" she snorted. "You look like a greased pig."

I discovered that I didn't look too bad if I was lighted properly, so I took to sitting in dim corners. One time I decided that in our house we would dine by candlelight. Accordingly, I set the table with a couple of chaste white tapers, telling myself happily that by their flickering light no one could tell the difference between me and Hedy Lamarr. When my husband came home for dinner, he was indeed astounded to find the dining room illumined only by candles. "What's the idea? Is it Halloween?" he asked cheerily. I told him, somewhat hesitantly, that I had thought it might be a nice idea to dine by candlelight. He was quite unimpressed. "It's too damn dark," he said. "I want to see what I'm eating." So I gave up that idea.

My mother, who at the time was sixty and still one of the most beautiful women I had ever seen, came to visit one day. She complained about my sluggishness and apathy. "You seem so down in the mouth, dear," she said. "Probably poor circulation. I don't think you get enough exercise. Why don't you take tap dancing? Or join a gym group?" Gym! I coudn't have been more shocked if she had suggested that I start smoking opium. Gym! Standing on my head, at my age! Me and Lady Mendl.

"Mother, I'm too old," I said, in a quiet, sad little voice.

"Oh, so you're too old?" said my mother, tartly. "Well, isn't that too bad? All right, Grandma. Tell me, what is the secret of your longevity? A quart of whiskey a day? Tell me about the time you sat on Abraham Lincoln's lap. Or was it the other way around?"

It was apparent that my own mother thought I was acting like a schnook. I decided that it was pretty mean of her, just because she, by some secret magic, had successfully defied old age and still had men leering at her every time she walked down the street. "All right," I told myself, "so she's a female Peter Pan. But me, I'm just middle-aged, that's all, and I have to face it. Well, being as old as I am has its compensations, I suppose."

I took to consoling myself in that fashion by constant reminders of the alleged advantages that accrue to those who are "getting on." For example, on crowded buses I would instinctively start to leap to my feet to give a middle-aged woman my seat and then I would remember, "Why, I'm a middle-aged woman *myself!* I don't have to give her my seat." And I would sit tight—comfortable, but not a great deal happier.

This state of affairs continued for some months, and then one day I woke up. I suddenly realized that nobody seemed to be treating me with any greater deference because of my incipient senility. No young girls on buses got up and gave me *their* seats. Little boys in the streets called out, "Miss! You dropped your glove." They hadn't switched it to "Lady!" Happily married though I was, I was pleased to note that men still looked at me with interest when I entered a bar or restaurant. And no young Eagle Scouts were moved to say, "Here, Granny, take my arm and let me help you across the street." I was shaken.

"What's wrong? What gives?" I asked myself. The answer was that although I definitely was forty, that age no longer has any particular meaning for a woman, unless it's a psychological handicap.

This is not only true of women in their forties but also of those in their fifties, and even, in some cases, in their sixties. Today we are surrounded by well-known women who are admittedly middle-aged in chronological terms yet still glamorous. Take a look at Joan Crawford, Joan Bennett, Barbara Stanwyck, Loretta Young, Lilli Palmer, Myrna Loy, Claudette Colbert, Arlene Francis, Katharine Hepburn, Ginger Rogers, Paulette Goddard, Gloria Swanson, and Marlene Dietrich, to name only a few. Most of them admit to being over fifty; at least two will never see sixty again. The list of youthful-looking forty-year-old beauties would fill a whole chapter.

The point is that these women are not only still successful as charmers in their professional careers. That could perhaps be explained away by make-up, lighting, and special photographic tricks. But the fact is that in their private lives they can still make the fellows jump through hoops. Those who are not married are dashing around pursued by admirers, wooed by rich, handsome, famous, eligible males, and holding their own against the younger crop of sirens when it comes to making masculine hearts go pitty-pat.

These are the famous examples, the ones whose pictures you see everywhere—and even in news shots they look good! But I know, and everyone else does, too, plenty of unpublicized women of forty or over, both career women and housewives, who simply do not look their age and are by no means ready to retire from the romantic arena.

It is not solely a matter of money for servants, facials, massage, clothes, luxurious surroundings, and breakfast in bed. All of that helps—but even without it the fact remains that the average American woman of forty is getting younger-looking all the time. It works two ways: as she looks younger, she feels younger; and as she feels younger, naturally she looks younger.

This was definitely not the case when I was a girl. Then, a forty-year-old woman was a middle-aged woman, and that was all there was to it. If there were exceptions who didn't look or act their age, you can be sure they didn't go around admitting it either.

Probably the first famous harbinger of the new era was Wallis Simpson, now the Duchess of Windsor. She was the one who officially began it all for American women. She was forty when the King of England gave up his throne in order to marry her, and when the full impact of this heartening event sank in, a whole generation of middle-aged American women were handed a new lease on life. They studied her photographs, took a look in their own mirrors, and said to themselves, "Well, why not?"

I am not advocating that every forty- or fifty-year-old woman should rush out and start looking for amorous adventures. I am merely pointing out that it is at least possible, if not practical. The woman of that age no longer need feel that she is a "has-been." Whether her life is happily filled with her home, her husband and her children; whether she is busy with job or career; whether she is otherwise occupied with hobbies or social life—she can still savor the marvelous morale stimulant of knowing that she is not an old relic at whom no man would give a second look. Furthermore, if she does happen to be widowed, divorced, or single, she can be physically attractive, with an excellent chance of finding happiness with someone.

French women and other European women in their middle years have long been recognized as redoubtable entries in the romance division. But this was not the case here in the United States prior to our Mrs. Simpson. One reason for this may have been that European women retained their interest in sex longer than did Americans. As a result, they took pains to care for their appearance and to make themselves attractive to men as long as possible. American women, on the other hand, tended to concentrate their energies on the appearance of their homes instead of their persons. Their dreams were not of lovers, but of Chippendale furniture or a shiny new refrigerator.

This was all very well in its way and no doubt was appreciated by their menfolk to a certain extent, but when you come right down to basic facts of life, slip covers and draperies, no matter how attractive, will never take the place in a man's heart of a wife with a smooth skin and a neat figure.

SOME OLD-TIME WRINKLE REMEDIES—
NOT RECOMMENDED

Some of the old-time remedies sound pretty rough. An early nineteenth century beauty book advised getting rid of wrinkles by mixing one spoonful of the best *tar* (although probably not the kind we use for paving roads, because the book said, "For the tar, apply to the druggist, who keeps it on hand for inhaling") in one pint of olive oil or almond oil, heating them together in a tin double boiler, stirring until smooth, and adding more oil if the mixture got too thick. When cool enough, it was applied to the face before going to bed. "The black, unpleasant mask washes off easily with warm water and soap," the book said reassuringly. Actually, the tar was made of fresh resin from pine and spruce trees, but I shudder at the mental picture of all those women getting into bed with their sticky faces. Boo!

The same source also stated that French women had long used turpentine "to erase the marks of age." They put thirty-six grains of turpentine in three drachms of alcohol and then allowed this mixture to dry on the face, making a kind of varnish which must have felt awful and smelled worse, not to mention what it could do to a sensitive skin. By all means don't try it.

I also read in one old beauty book that in Bohemia "countesses over thirty" went to arsenic springs to make their skin youthful. It didn't say whether the treatment worked as well for anyone who wasn't a countess. In our own Virginia, in the last century, there were said to be women over eighty with pink and white skins and not a wrinkle who owed it all to the use of rose water and glycerine, with a few drops of carbolic acid. I am all in favor of the rose water and glycerine—although I can't guarantee that it'll keep you wrinkle-free at eighty!—but I would be leery of the carbolic acid, although I do know that in my younger days there was a popular commercial skin cleanser which contained a small amount of it. Also carbolic acid is used today in many healing ointments, but I wouldn't want to monkey around mixing it up myself. A druggist could advise you.

Here are some other old-time remedies for wrinkles and lines:

One dating from the time of Charles II was said to "obliterate wrinkles as far as anything can beside enamel."

Boil gum benzoin in spirits of wine till it forms a rich tincture. Put fifteen drops in a glass of water. This makes a milky liquid. Use it to bathe your face, neck and arms. Let it dry on the skin.

This one, also for removing wrinkles, is from the days of Queen Victoria:

2 ounces juice of onions
2 ounces white lily extract (or crushed white lily)
2 ounces honey
1 ounce pure white wax from a pharmacy

Put all the ingredients in a new earthen pipkin (earthenware pot or casserole) and stir over fire until the wax is melted. Remove pipkin from fire and continue stirring briskly until the mixture cools. This should be applied before going to bed and allowed to remain on until morning.

RECOMMENDED WRINKLE TREATMENT

Actually, the chief cosmetic method to delay premature wrinkles and even sometimes temporarily to erase little lines is to oil and moisturize the skin. Women used to use skunk oil with camphor in it, goose grease, and bear oil. Those aren't so easy to come by today, but mink oil has suddenly become popular, especially in France. I don't know about its efficacy, but I do know it's expensive. A simpler and much cheaper treatment is to rub the face daily with castor oil or with olive oil. The latter has been used by women all the way back to Cleopatra, and even before her.

Many women recommend steaming the face first—using the steam from a teakettle spout or a basin of boiling water—and then oiling it. In London, many fashionable beauties patronize a well-known sauna bath where the finishing touch is a facial and body massage with almond oil, another old-time favorite.

The treatment for flabby skin described in Chapter 6 has also been used as an anti-wrinkle preparation for many years.

Another harmless, old-fashioned preventive treatment for wrinkles is to soak in a hot tub and apply cod-liver oil generously over the neck and face, with particular attention to the area around the eyes. The heat from the tub encourages the oil to sink into the skin.

Several women have told me that they prefer to use honey to penetrate the outer skin layer and nourish the inner skin. They recommend the honey-and-egg mask for this. Mix well one tablespoon of pure honey and the beaten white of one egg. Spread over the face and leave on for fifteen minutes. Then wash off with tepid water. Said to have been Lucrezia Borgia's favorite beauty secret. This is an excellent beauty mask for toning up the skin, but I tend to favor the use of oils as an anti-wrinkle method.

One simple old-time favorite, enthusiastically endorsed by women who use it today, is to smear the face with real fresh cream, leave on for ten minutes, and then lightly wipe off with a soft towel or absorbent cotton before going to bed. In the morning, you should cleanse the skin thoroughly with tepid water.

The one thing *not* to do—because it dries up the natural oils—is to expose your skin to too much sun. No woman over the age of thirty-five should go in for prolonged sun bathing. She may look great while the tan lasts, but just wait till it begins to fade and then see how old and withered her poor skin looks! Besides, overexposure tends to enlarge the pores.

CROWS' FEET AND WRINKLED EYELIDS

The little lines around the eyes called "crows' feet" can often be improved by a treatment handed down in French families and used today by many French women:

Every morning when you wash your face hold a cold wash cloth against your closed eyes for a couple of minutes. Then every morning for ten days dip a finger in an anti-wrinkle cream and lightly massage the lines going from the outer corner of the eye toward the temple. Always do the massage in the same direction as the lines, horizontally, never up and down.

An anti-wrinkle cream for crows' feet can be made by preparing this recipe:

Buy one pound of pure raw lanolin at the drugstore and a small bottle of oil of sweet almond. Melt the lanolin in a double boiler and slowly add enough sweet almond oil to make an esay-to-spread cream. You can use as much of the oil as you like, but don't get the mixture too liquid. The idea is to have it come out the consistency of a rich cold cream. This also makes a great cream to use all over—face, neck, elbows, hands and even feet.

When you're using it just for the crows' feet, you can wear it even in the daytime under dark glasses. Or instead of this cream you can use any of the oils mentioned before: castor oil, olive oil, mineral oil, or plain white petroleum jelly.

Each night before going to bed, after you have removed your make-up, stick on the crows' feet a piece of adhesive tape and leave on all night. This is an old French trick for getting rid of crows' feet (which the French call "goose feet"), but in order to make it work you have to stretch the skin with two fingers of one hand so that the wrinkles are eliminated. Then, holding the skin thus taut and smooth, stick on the adhesive with the other hand. (Put one finger near the outer end of your eyebrow and the other about an inch below it, and spread them apart to stretch the skin.)

Another French trick for wrinkled eyelids is to take a slice of raw potato and grate it onto cheese cloth or surgical gauze. Put this over your whole eye (close it first, of course) and leave on for fifteen minutes if it does not irritate the skin. Some women are allergic to it.

An alternative compress can be made by soaking the gauze in freshly squeezed orange juice and applying in the same way, keeping the gauze wet with juice, for half an hour.

GRAY HAIR

I am aware that lots of people say they love white hair. I don't. I think it makes any woman look older than she needs to look. Even worse than white hair is gray hair. Fortunately, it is a simple and fairly inexpensive thing for a woman to tint her hair today, and it is so common that no one thinks anything of it or goes around—as they used to do—whispering behind her back, "Do you think she *dyes* her hair?" in the same scandalized tones as if they were asking, "Do you think she takes dope?"

That is, it is a simple thing for *almost* all women. Some women, however, are allergic to all dyes and tints. I am one of them. Some time ago, I started to get a little gray at the temples, so I thought I'd go and have it touched up. Now there is a law that requires hairdressers to pre-test tints before applying them. The customer is supposed to go and have some of the mixture rubbed behind her ear and then go back twenty-four hours later. If she is at all allergic, the spot behind the ear will be inflamed and the tint should not be used. However, so few women have this allergy (although apparently enough of

them to have made the law necessary) that sometimes the beauty shops get careless and don't bother
with the test. This happened to me. They touched
up my gray hairs and I was delighted with the result until a couple of days later when my face and
whole head started to swell. Naturally, I was terri-
fied. I rushed to see my dermatologist friend, who
gave me injections of cortisone, in case the poison
had gotten into my blood stream, and said that it
could have killed me. I had to sit around the house
for the next week covered with wet compresses until my head was reduced from pumpkin shape to
normal size again.

Aside from the discomfort—and the fright it gave
me—I was then faced with the problem of what to
do about my gray hairs in the future. For a time, I
contented myself with trying to pluck them out with
eyebrow tweezers, but after a while I could see that
I was fighting a losing battle this way. I was resigned
to looking like Barbara Fritchie—"Shoot if you must
this old gray head!"

Then a few years ago I discovered a preparation
to use at home for restoring the hair to its natural
color, whatever shade that might be. I tried it and
have been using it ever since. It's inexpensive, quite
easy to use, and absolutely harmless. You buy it in
drugstores and it's called Canute Water. It's not perfect—that is to say, it's not as simple as having your
hair tinted by a good professional—but it beats nothing all hollow. I pass this information along in case
there might be some other women who are allergic
to the regular commercial dyes. Use it according to
the directions. It restores the hair to its original natural color—or a reasonable approximation.

Incidentally, this is a very good thing for men who
don't want to have gray hair but who wouldn't be
caught dead going to have their hair dyed.

A century or more ago, before commercial dyes
were invented, some women were as loath to see
their hair turn gray as they are today. Accordingly,

they tried various remedies, among them rubbing the head with pure sperm oil from whales or with bear's grease, although by the nineteenth century this last was getting harder to get. "One can never be sure of getting the real article," lamented one beauty book.

Failing that, another early dye was obtained by pouring one quart of boiling water on two heaping tablespoons of rock salt, and the resulting solution was used when cold. Still another, said to be a speedy and harmless dye for the hair and eyebrows, was to use the water in which potatoes had been boiled with their skins on. I was tempted to try this when I was in Europe for a year and ran out of Canute Water, but it's pretty difficult to boil potatoes in a hotel room.

A similar old-time hair darkener was used by the great-grandmother of a friend of mine, but I don't know how successfully. She boiled the potato parings alone, strained off the water, dipped a fine-toothed comb in this and kept drawing it through her hair where the gray was. If not satisfied with the first attempt, she repeated it, using a sponge to apply the water. Exposing the hair to outdoor sunlight was supposed to darken and set the dye. She had to wear something to protect her dress and she was also careful to wipe off immediately any of the water on her forehead and neck, as apparently the potato peeling water made a pretty indelible stain.

These things may not be quite as silly as they sound. I suppose there are certain minerals in the potato skins that do the trick—perhaps the same ingredients that are used in my Canute Water, for all I know.

I also came across two other recipes that claimed to restore the original color of the hair and also to be good for the scalp. One was very simple: mix one teaspoonful of carbonate of ammonia in one quart of water and bathe the hair with it.

The other, more elaborate, was:

1 ounce tincture of acetate of iron
1 pint water
1/2 ounce glycerine
5 grains sulphuret of potassium

Mix well and let the bottle stand uncorked. Rub a little into the hair daily. (The recipe adds that the potassium has "a foul smell" and that it might therefore be a good idea to add a few drops of attar of roses.) I can't vouch for either of these last two recipes, as I don't know anyone who has actually tried them.

Finally, one of the most famous hair darkeners of them all was sage tea, steeped and applied to the hair. This was probably more common than anything else, as well as perfectly harmless, and many a lady in olden times disguised the tell-tale gray hairs in this manner, although she made sure to do it in secret. Fortunately, times have changed, and today practically no woman has to have gray hair unless she really insists on it.

THE FIGURE

Heaven knows a trim figure helps to preserve the appearance of youth. A few women are lucky enough to keep their waistline effortlessly, but sooner or later, to most of us, comes the horrible moment when we discover that the waistbands of our skirts are a mite too tight, that our belts are no longer comfortable when fastened in the customary notch, and that our figures have begun to take on a distressing resemblance to rectangles.

This is known as the beginning of "middle-age spread," although all too often it happens to younger women as well. If you want to keep looking young as long as possible, you have to take care of your figure as well as your face. This book deals only with old-time beauty secrets, so I am not going to go into the subject of diet and exercise except to say that we did not invent the diet, even though sometimes we seem to have carried it to the point of mania. In olden times, women also went on diets, but the reason was usually not to lose weight (they liked them plumper in those days) but to improve the health or benefit the complexion. Thus, in old-fashioned beauty books, women were advised to go on an annual diet of vegetables, cooked fruits and water during the forty days of Lent as a special treatment to clear the skin, not to improve the figure.

One of these books tells of a beautiful French baroness at the court of King Louis Philippe who lived entirely on oranges for forty years! This was certainly the longest crash diet of all time. At the age of eighty-four, the baroness was said to have the brilliant eyes and fresh skin of a young girl. She ate one dozen oranges for breakfast, another dozen for lunch, and for dinner still another dozen, plus a slice of bread and a glass of Bordeaux wine. The book adds, "I advise no one to put themselves on this diet, but it is certain that the most beautiful women are, generally, as temperate as camels."

Another famous dieter, this one a nineteenth century French marquise who lived to be almost a hundred, for fifty years ate only grilled compotes and vegetables cooked in chicken broth. She drank nothing but water, except during periods of pregnancy when her doctors required her to take sweetened wine. During the last forty years of her life, a little candied sugar was added to her drinking water.

These were isolated cases, of course. Most of our ancestors didn't bother with diets or with exercise but accepted plumpness as one of the normal attributes of middle age. It was not until the late nineteenth and early twentieth centuries that dieting began to be fashionable and then it usually took the simple form of going without food for a day or so at a time. A little later, there came a fad for reducing pills, and I remember one horrible story current in my childhood. I can't believe that it was true, but I heard it repeated many times. It was said that there was a certain pill which enabled women to eat everything they wanted and at the same time get thin. Women who took this pill, so the story went, developed ravenous appetites, but the more they ate, the thinner they became. Finally, an investigation revealed that the pills contained small tapeworms. When the pills were swallowed the tapeworms remained alive in the intestines, where they lived happily while the women gorged themselves, grew thinner and thinner, and eventually died.

I suppose that the genesis of this ghastly tale may have been the popularity of patented reducing pills with a harmful effect and that the story was spread with the aim of discouraging their use. I am sure not a word of it was true, but it certainly scared the daylights out of *me*, and to this day I won't touch any pills, powders, or liquids advertised as aids to reducing. (Incidentally, in France a couple of years ago there were 682 different reducing products on the market.)

The best procedure, before embarking on any strenuous course of diet or exercise, is to consult your doctor. There are many helpful and sensible books on diet and exercise. The thing to bear in mind is to use common sense—and also to remember that almost no men really like the emaciated, angular, fashion-model type of figure that seems to be our national goal.

As I said before, the modern, up-to-date diets and exercises do not lie within the province of this book. I only mention the subject because no discussion of how to preserve a youthful appearance can omit all reference to the figure. Also, of course, diet and exercise can help to keep your skin young, along with the faithful use of proper oils and creams.

WHEN ALL ELSE FAILS

Most of us can't afford plastic surgery, and I

wouldn't want to try it even if I could. It may be different for an actress, whose livelihood depends on preserving her looks, but for those of us whose faces are not their fortunes, I think the best thing is to try to grow old as gracefully and as gradually as possible, without resorting to any drastic experiments. When I was a child, they used to inject paraffin into the skin—the actress Edna Wallace Hopper was one of the women who admitted have it done—but this was a pretty unsatisfactory method, as the paraffin eventually melted or dissolved or something, leaving the face looking worse than ever. The whole idea of injections gives me the creeps. It seems to me that the way to combat the ravages of the years is to try to take sensible care of your skin without going to extremes. The white of egg mask or the honey or meal masks will help to keep your skin firm, while the use of oils will aid in making it wrinkle-resistant. Plenty of rest and sleep also help to keep you young-looking. Then, when at last the wrinkles finally come, just try to accept them with good grace and make the best of it. After all, it happens to everyone who lives long enough.

Some women who really worry about looking old are careful to do little things that disguise the signs of age. They know that they look more youthful by candlelight or other soft light, and that wearing a hat with a veil covers up the lines. They don't wear strapless dresses or shorts if their skin has that crepey look, and they tend to stick to high necks and long sleeves. All this sort of thing is just camouflage, of course, but it can help. What it can't do is eliminate the wrinkles if they are already there. The point I want to make is that it's no longer necessary to give up and throw in the sponge just because you may have passed your fortieth birthday. If you've been taking care of your looks before then you've little to worry about. If you haven't, it's still not too late to start.

As Constance Bennett, the actress, once said, "I

intend to remain between thirty and forty, because I think that *the twenty-five years* between thirty and forty are the most interesting in a woman's life!" And with a little reasonable care they often can be.

14

Making the Most of Perfume

She walked into the room and all the men went mad with desire. Naturally, she was wearing Mysterious Sin of Oriental Love, that pulsating perfume of surrender, the fabulous secret of which was known only to one ancient queen in Outer Mongolia. (And what a gay old time of it *she* had!)

Such is life in the perfume advertisements. The perfume industry spends thousands of dollars every year on this type of advertisement, and the end result has been that many women seldom buy perfume or even use it when it is given to them.

This is too bad, because perfume can be a pleasant, lovely thing. Since the earliest recorded times, it has been an integral part of a woman's cosmetic kit, indispensable as an aid to her attractiveness and a weapon in the arsenal of feminine charm. Most of the good scents have always been compounded of nature's own ingredients: the essence of flowers and the animal essences—civet, musk and ambergris. If you want to, you can blend your own fragrance, and some women still do this. Even if you prefer to buy it ready-made, there are certain tricks to stretch the use of a bottle of perfume. I'll give you some of these later on.

The reason women don't use perfume as much as they could is because the type of advertising used by the manufacturers has conditioned us to look upon it as something solely connected with sex, only to be worn when we are out to make a killing. We have also been taught to regard it as so fabulous, costly and precious that it seems an extravagant luxury, to be used a few drops at a time and to be hoarded carefully until the fragrance has all evaporated (which happens fairly quickly once a bottle has been opened, because most perfumes have an alcohol base).

The majority of American women do not buy perfume for themselves. They don't even buy their own toilet water and cologne, although they are doing so more than they did a dozen years ago. At that time, a survey conducted by a research group called the Psychological Corporation showed that approximately seventy-one per cent of the colognes and toilet waters used by women came to them as gifts. An even higher percentage of perfumes were gifts, and of these more than sixty per cent were gifts from men.

Another survey, made recently by the Fragrance Foundation, revealed that the situation has not improved much. The Foundation reported that women still consider perfume a somewhat daring luxury, to be used only on special occasions. The survey showed that only one-half of one per cent of American women use fragrance every day, and that sixty to sixty-five per cent of all perfume sold is bought by men as gifts for women. Approximately one-half of the total money spent annually for fragrance is spent at three periods: Christmas time, Valentine's Day, and Mother's Day.

The perfume makers are worried, hurt, and puzzled. Here they have a product which almost all women love and want—and almost none of them will buy. It is not something like a sable coat or a diamond bracelet, obviously beyond the purchasing power of the average woman. It is not something rare and hard to get, like hummingbirds' tongues. It is not even forbidden, like aigrette feathers or absinthe. It's done up in pretty packages; it's on sale in every drugstore and women's store; and everybody's heard of it. Yet it is a fact that in one year alone more perfume was brought into the United States by people who bought it in foreign cities than was sold in the entire country.

An interesting sidelight on this was the information that many women bring home perfume from Europe and then take it to some local store where they claim that it was originally purchased as a gift, which they would like to return. In this way, they pick up a small profit, because they would have paid, say, ten dollars for the bottle in Paris, and it retails in their home town for maybe twenty dollars. The result is that baffled storekeepers, come inventory time, sometimes find themselves in possession of more bottles of perfume than they started out with.

As I say, the situation is improving today, but not fast enough. It is time to stop this one-drop-and-he'll-fall-at-your-feet nonsense. Perfume is not a love potion. It will help to make you more attractive, but it is not something with which, like chloroform, you overcome a man. Years ago, the manufacturers pounced on the idea of sex and they have ridden it into the ground. They have hammered away at the idea that if a woman wears perfume she'll get her man; and that if a man gives a woman perfume she'll surrender without a struggle. They have just about put it in the same category with Spanish Fly.

Here are a few of the slogans used in past years:
"It's the magic by which every man is bewitched."
"Voices of prophecy . . . whispering, 'We will know each other better . . .' The lure of anticipation . . ."
"The forbidden perfume."

"A four-century-old legend of fabulous allure. A subtle, stirring fragrance-echo of the sixteenth century."

But it hasn't worked out the way they hoped. Americans, always somewhat inhibited about sex, have demurred at the idea of wearing for everyday use something which has been represented to them as a powerful aphrodisiac. Especially not in the daytime!

There is no reason why perfume promotion should not be slanted directly to the housewife. I don't necessarily mean pictures of beaming women in frilly aprons, surrounded by refrigerators, washing machines, apple pies, and small children shouting, "Gee, Mommy, you smell wonderful!" But it could be done —and should be—in such a way that the average woman would feel that it is all right to wear fragrance every day without feeling like a combination of Jezebel and Madame Pompadour.

I feel that some of the names are a little embarrassing, too, especially ones like My Sin, Surrender, Indiscreet, Aphrodisia, Shocking, Secret of Venus, and Tigress. I used to use My Sin all the time until I just couldn't stand such a silly name any longer. People would ask me what it was, and I would bridle and say, "My Sin," and they would give me a "How's-that-again?" look.

Other manufacturers, struggling to get out of the exotic-sex trap, have burned their copies of *Roget's Thesaurus* and, in desperation, adopted numbers: No. 44, No. 9, No. 5, No. 22. I think this is a mistake, too. Perfume *is* beautiful and glamorous, and there is nothing in the world more feminine, so why reduce it to numbers that sound like signals for football plays or a new scientific formula for the treatment of the common cold? "What is that wonderful perfume you're wearing?" "Oh, that's Formula No. 896."

The job of naming new odors has become only slightly less related to the occult mysteries than naming new Pullman cars used to be. I can just picture the Board of Directors sitting around their long, polished table, ears alert, brows furrowed by the strain, as they consider the choices submitted to them. Name after name is solemnly considered and rejected. Then another name is called out, and their faces light up with triumph. "That's it, men! By George, we've got it!" And what have they got? Some exotic name which no one knows exactly how to pronounce, and which no one has ever heard of before. Well, that means they will have to explain it in the advertising. It's the name of a fabulous Arabian prince . . .

So they're off to a good start. The perfume is advertised with a large drawing showing a white horse galloping madly through what seems to be a sandstorm, while on his back, perched at a perilous angle which would make him the hit of any rodeo, clings the prince, one arm around an exceedingly well-developed girl who is obviously swooning with rapture and is clad only in an extraordinarily transparent wisp of white chiffon—just the costume for an early morning canter. The copy beneath the picture goes on and on, hinting at magic sex charms this perfume gave to the women in the prince's exotic court, and ends with the sentence, "You can believe, when you wear the prince's perfume, that *tonight* anything might happen."

Well! I don't see how they could expect that any woman, after reading through this sort of thing, would have the nerve to go out and buy the stuff. Even I, who love perfume, would hesitate at that one. As a housewife and mother of two, the last thing in the world I would contemplate buying is a perfume that would drive men insane with lust. Then the perfume industry sits around and worries and makes clucking noises and wonders why women don't rush out and buy more perfume and use it every day, around the house, or at the office, or when doing their shopping!

117

The perfume may well be a magnificent scent but by presenting it as something so rare, so mysterious, so exotic, brought all the way from the ends of the earth, the net impression given to the woman reader is that it is something more precious than her life's blood, to be used one drop at a time for special occasions such as, we assume, her coronation in Westminster Abbey.

One or two perfumers, in striving to escape the sex angle, have taken to describing their scents as "witty," as if they were trying to sell Groucho Marx in a bottle. Others go in for long historical data: the beauty secrets of ancient queens, the travels of Marco Polo, chemists growing gray bending over their retorts. I don't want a perfume that I have to *explain* to people, and I don't care whether they found the formula buried under an altar in Tibet or worked it out in a streamlined factory in New Jersey. I just want one that makes me smell good.

But the picture isn't completely black. Today, there seems to be a trend toward a more subtle approach in advertising, and even toward uncomplicated names. Some perfumers are content to call their products by the name of the key flower odor—violet, gardenia, jasmine, rose, lily-of-the-valley, lilac, carnation, etc.—and I am all for this, because it's not only attractive but it also gives you an idea of what the scent is like.

Women should be taught to wear perfume or cologne every day. It not only gives pleasure to other people, but it gives a lift to the woman who wears it. It makes her feel feminine. Because it is the most personal of all accessories, she should wear only a scent which she herself likes. The first perfume survey I mentioned earlier showed that over eighteen per cent of the women questioned disliked the perfumes they had received as gifts. One reason for this is that no one else can tell for sure whether or not a perfume is suitable for you. An odd fact about perfume is that the scent often changes on different women because the chemistry of their skin affects the fragrance. A perfume does not smell the same on an oily skin as it does on a dry one.

My own favorite perfume story deals with the time a man gave me a bottle of the same scent used by an actress with whom he had once been in love. He had been raving for weeks about this deliriously seductive fragrance and finally he broke down and bought me a bottle of it, presumably with the idea that I, too, could become irresistible. Well, I put a lot on one night and waited breathlessly for him to call for me, as we were going to the theatre. When he came into my apartment, he didn't seem to react properly, so I asked him gaily, "Don't you smell anything?" He sniffed anxiously for a moment, like a hunting dog, and then his whole face lit up with pleasure. "Ummmm!" he said. "Brussels sprouts!"

Another time, years ago, I used a lovely rose fragrance which was then being advertised as guaranteed to make men go mad with desire. Unfortunately, all it did to my beau was to make him go mad with hay fever.

As a general rule, the wisest thing is to choose your own perfume and to wear the one which is most pleasing to you and to those around you. No perfume is dirt cheap, but you don't have to buy the most expensive ones on the market. Remember, there's a big mark-up in this product, as there is in all the beauty preparations. Many of the less expensive scents are lovely and effective.

One way to stretch perfume is to mix it with toilet water of the same scent. Or just use the cologne, which is always far cheaper than the perfume. In the case of my own favorite scent, Aphrodisia, I like the cologne better than I do the perfume, and I find that the odor lasts just about as long. You get a much larger bottle for a lot less money, and you can feel freer in its use. I like to spray it on, as this makes me feel very luxurious and *femme fatale,* but I admit that this is more wasteful than rubbing it on with your finger tips.

Gabrielle Chanel, the famous French *couturière,* whose Chanel No. 5 is the most famous perfume in the world, says you should put perfume on "every place you expect to be kissed." However, most experts suggest a dab behind each ear, some on the throat and under the arms, and a touch on the inside curves of your arms and on your wrists. But not too much, especially if it's a strong perfume essence. The idea is to attract a man, not suffocate him.

Never throw away your empty scent bottles. Put them in your drawers with your underclothes. Leave the stoppers off and put them in the drawers, too. They will perfume your clothing for months.

Another trick is to put the scent on a little swab of absorbent cotton and pin it to the inside of your brassiere, where the heat of your body helps to bring out the fragrance. Don't throw away these swabs as long as they have any lingering fragrance left in them. Put them in your drawers, too.

An old-fashioned trick which is still used is to make sachets and put them in the drawer, inside of gloves, stockings, and handkerchiefs. Some women also put sachets in their clothes closets, attaching them by ribbons or pins to the hangers so that they are inside the dresses. You can put perfume on absorbent cotton pads for this purpose, or you can make sachets by filling little bags of silk with a sachet powder. By thus delicately perfuming everything you wear, you don't need to use as much actual perfume on your body from day to day.

A favorite sachet recipe from grandma's time was this:

> 4 ounces orris root, coarsely powdered
> 3 ounces cassia
> 2 ounces cloves
> 12 grams powdered ambergris
> 12 grams musk seed
> 1/2 ounce cedar-wood sawdust
> 1/2 ounce sandalwood

Mix thoroughly, and add:

> 2 drams oil of lavender
> 2 drams oil of bergamot
> 2 drams attar of roses

The beauty of making your own sachets is that you don't have to stick to this recipe. You can add any perfume you prefer—oil of jasmine, rose, violet, whatever scent you like. (As with the cold creams, if your druggist doesn't have the ingredients, he can order them for you or tell you where to get them. Many women make their own perfumes, and there are wholesale companies and importers where you can buy the ingredients you want.)

Also, you can, if you like, leave out the cloves or any of the other ingredients as long as you have a coarse powder, like orris, or pulverized reindeer moss (called Cyprus powder), or some such base which will absorb the perfume essence.

Here is an old-fashioned recipe for lavender sachet:

> 1 pound powdered lavender (It doesn't have to be *powdered;* it can be the regular crushed lavender)
> 1/4 pound powdered gum benzoin
> 6 ounces oil of lavender

Put the mixture into little silk bags. Many women like to keep these in their linen closets, as they give a delightful odor to sheets and pillow cases.

Orris root seems to have a violet smell, as many of the old-time recipes for violet scents would indicate. Here are some of them:

VIOLET SACHET POWDER

> 8 ounces powdered orris root
> 5 drops oil of bergamot
> 3 drops oil of bitter almonds
> 4 drops oil of rose
> 1 dram tincture of musk

Mix thoroughly.

VIOLET BATH BAGS

>   2 pounds finely ground oatmeal
>   3 ounces almond meal
>   1 cake castile soap, finely shaved
> 1/4 pound powdered orris root

Mix all the ingredients together and put into bags which you can make of cheese cloth. Use them instead of wash cloths in the bath.

VIOLET BATH LOTION

> 4 ounces alcohol
> 1 ounce ammonia
> 1 dram essence of violets

Pour some of this into the bath water. It not only perfumes it but softens the water.

VIOLETTES DU BOIS PERFUME

> 5 ounces essence of violets
> 1 ounce essence of acacia
> 1 ounce essence of rose
> 1 ounce extract of iris root
> 5 drops oil of bitter almonds

VIOLET TOILET WATER

> 1-3/4 ounces essence of violet
>   1/2 ounce essence of rose
>   1/2 ounce essence of cassia
>   14 ounces alcohol

Oil of rose geranium, or other scents, can be used in place of the violet. Perfumed bath salts can be made by mixing three or four drams of oil of rose, oil of lavender, oil of jasmine, or whatever your favorite scent is, with fourteen ounces of bicarbonate of soda and two ounces of potassium carbonate. Put a tablespoonful into the bath.

Women even used to perfume their kid gloves. They mixed four drops of extract of ambergris with two ounces of spirits of wine and rubbed the inside of their gloves with a sponge or piece of linen dipped in the mixture. Many French women also perfumed the insides of their shoes in this manner and also their corsets.

A famous old perfume method was called Peau d'Espagne. I doubt if many modern women would want to go to the trouble of making it, but here it is:

PEAU d'ESPAGNE

Soak small pieces of chamois, or white kid, in the following solution for three or four days:

    4 drams oil of rose, synthetic
    4 drams oil of neroli, synthetic
    4 drams oil of sandalwood
    2 drams oil of lavender
    2 drams oil of lemon
   30 minims oil of cinnamon
    2 drams lindalyl acetate
   12 grains cumarin
    1 dram artificial musk
    3 ounces tincture of benzoin

Remove the leather from the liquid, drain it, and spread it on glass to dry. Coat the rough side of the leather with the following mixture, applied with a brush:

      2 drams sublimated benzoic acid
     12 grains musk
     12 grains civet
  6-1/2 drams gum arabic
      5 drams glycerine
  1-1/2 ounces water

123

Rub the musk and civet thoroughly with the acid and gum, then blend in the glycerine and water to form a smooth mixture. After coating the rough side of the leather with this, fold the leather over—the two halves will stick to each other—and let dry. This perfumed skin was said to give off its odor for years and was used by women instead of sachet bags in trunks, closets, wardrobes, drawers, and glove and handkerchief boxes.

It seems to me that there ought to be a simpler way of achieving the same effect. When I get around to it, maybe I'll experiment with putting my favorite perfume on bits of chamois and see how it works.

Some women today get their individual perfumes not by mixing them from scratch but by buying them and then mixing different odors until they get a scent they like which is all their own. Whatever method you use, a pleasant odor is one of the most attractive things about a woman. We can't all look like movie sirens, but at least we can smell as nice as they do!

❀ ❀ 15

Beauty Secrets
of Famous Women

Often we do not learn the beauty secrets of famous women until after they are dead, and not always then. Most women are pretty cagey when it comes to revealing the means by which they retain and enhance their looks. This is above all true of women who are famous for their beauty. They like to pretend that it's all just sheer luck.

The most notable exceptions are the carrot juice set. These raw vegetable addicts are so fervently devoted to their diets that they spread the gospel far and wide, ever seeking new converts. Thus we all know, for example, that Greta Garbo has been on this health food kick for years, and it has to be admitted that her appearance is a potent testimonial to the benefits thereof.

The qualities in raw fruits and vegetables that make them so beneficial when taken internally are the same ones that do a beautifying job when applied externally. Garbo started using vegetable masks and other natural ingredients on her face when she was in her thirties, and the result of these treatments, combined with her eating habits, is that she has been able to retain her looks to a surprising degree. She uses almost no make-up, and her skin is firm and clear. The one cosmetic she is never without is mascara, and a photographer who knows her told me that in applying it she uses a favorite trick of actresses and models: powder the lashes first, then put on the mascara, then powder the lashes again and put more mascara on top of that. It makes the lashes look thicker.

Gloria Swanson is another famous beauty who advocates raw vegetables both *on* the face and *in* it; and she certainly looks marvelous, even though she is over sixty. So does Chanel, the French dress designer. That is, she looks great when you consider her age. She doesn't look beautiful, the way Garbo and Swanson do, but she could pass for a woman in her late fifties, which is pretty good for someone who is around eighty.

There is undoubtedly a lot to be said in favor of these health food diets. I can take the raw vegetables and the fresh fruits, but I draw the line at blackstrap molasses and I can't stand yogurt. I hate buttermilk, too, and that's supposed to be wonderful for you. The trouble with so many of these health foods, as far as I'm concerned, is that they simply are not appetizing. When I was a young girl, there was a fad for eating raw yeast. It came in little cakes wrapped in tin foil (maybe it still does), and you were supposed to spread it on crackers. Eaten regularly, it was said to do marvels for the complexion. I tried it valiantly but gave up after the first week. It's just too bad that fudge sundaes aren't as beneficial!

Here are some old-fashioned beauty secrets used by several famous women:

Betty Furness, of television fame, recommends using Crisco to remove make-up. She says that she finds it beneficial for the complexion. Crisco, of course, is pure vegetable oil.

Marlene Dietrich uses pure lanolin on her face, neck, and hands. She is certainly one of the most glamorous examples in the world of how young and beautiful a woman in her sixties can look if she takes the proper care of herself.

Virginia Martin, the voluptuous actress who starred in the Broadway musical "Little Me," takes Epsom salts baths to relax and loosen up her body muscles. Mix a few handfuls of Epsom salts in a tub of warm water and soak yourself in it.

Candy Jones, formerly a famous fashion model, recommends a whipped-cream facial. Just whip up fresh cream and spread it on the face, rubbing it in. Rinse off with tepid water, followed by cool.

Candy also advises women to rinse their hair in tea and put starch in their bath water—two well-known old-time beauty hints.

Joan Crawford often lies down for half an hour with wet tea bags on her eyes to brighten and rest them. Another favorite Crawford beauty secret is to drink a jigger of apple cider vinegar just before meals, to help her keep her slim figure. I've seen her order it at New York's famous "21" Restaurant and drink it down straight, without even making a face, which is more than I could do.

No one works harder than Joan at keeping herself in shape. She takes marvelous care of herself, and it pays off; she is still a smashingly attractive woman. Part of this is due to her meticulous grooming. Whenever she appears in public, she always looks every inch The Star. But I have seen her in her own home, without a touch of make-up on, and even then she still looks astoundingly youthful. She is blessed with a good facial bone structure—she has the most beautiful nose I have ever seen—and this is a big help to her in preserving her looks, but it would not be enough without the aid of her own intelligent beauty care.

In addition to the daily care of her hair and skin (years ago, she used to use petroleum jelly on her face, and so did Carole Lombard), she does regular exercises. Her favorite is the following:

Lie flat on your back on the floor. Lift both legs—feet together and knees straight, if possible—up, up, up, until your toes touch the floor behind your head.

Then lower your legs again, very, very slowly—as slowly as you can—until they reach the starting position. This is a superb exercise for the abdomen. You'll never have a big tummy if you do this one regularly, but it's not easy. In fact it's one of the hardest exercises I know. When your feet get down toward the floor, as you are lowering your legs, it takes tremendous effort and control to keep them moving slowly instead of just letting them go kerplop. Joan can do this exercise five or ten times in a row, but that takes plenty of practice, and more discipline than most of us have.

Speaking of the abdomen, in the latter part of the thirties there was a little book called *The Culture of the Abdomen* which was popular in London (the novelist Arnold Bennett wrote a blurb for the jacket, praising it to the skies) among men as well as women. It gave exercises for losing weight and improving the general health and appearance through exercising the stomach muscles. Condé Nast, the publisher of *Vogue*, became an enthusiast after a trip to London and presented copies of it to all the glamorous society and theatrical beauties of his acquaintance, as well as the *Vogue* models, and soon he had lovely women all over New York busily rotating their abdominal muscles, like so many cooch dancers. I know of a few who have kept up the exercises, and I must say they work. I remember one of them you could do sitting down (that's the kind of exercise *I* like!) and it consisted of drawing in your stomach and then letting it out again. You have to pretend that you are rotating it: in, up, over, out, down, over, in, up, etc. Keep it up slowly, as if you were turning your stomach over and over like a chicken on a rotisserie spit. It's really very good for you, although I don't quite go along with the book when it says that it's an exercise you can do *anywhere*. I can just see myself doing it on the bus.

If few women do their exercises in public, even fewer take care of their complexions outside of their own bathrooms. Nor do they reveal their secrets. I do know, however, that for years Clare Boothe Luce, the beautiful ex-editor, ex-playwright, ex-Congresswoman, ex-Ambassador—you name it, she's done it —used nothing on her face but Physicians and Surgeons soap, and she has one of the loveliest complexions in the land. I saw her on a South Carolina plantation, in the brilliant morning sun, with no make-up on, and there wasn't a line or a blemish (or even, apparently, a pore) in that delicate, translucent, ever youthful skin.

Drinking a cup or glass of hot water with lemon juice before breakfast is a favorite old-time beauty recipe of women all over. I first heard about it from Valentina, the attractive Russian who used to be America's most expensive *couturière*. We were at a luncheon given by Condé Nast in the French Pavilion at the 1939 World's Fair, and the famous singers Grace Moore and Gladys Swarthout were present, as was the Grand Duchess Marie of Russia. Valentina was indoctrinating everyone with the hot-water-and-lemon-juice theory. She said it was marvelous for the complexion, and I have followed her advice ever since.

Incidentally, Grace Moore used to rub castor oil on her face and neck every day. She said it was a favorite trick of many actresses whom she knew. Keeps away the wrinkles. She also confided that she kept her golden hair healthy and lustrous by massaging a little petroleum jelly into her scalp and then brushing her hair thoroughly. Still another of her beauty secrets was a diet. Like most singers, she had to fight against overweight. She told me that she lost forty pounds in six months by just giving up all potatoes, breads, desserts —and by not drinking any liquids with her meals.

The exquisite young American fashion model Johanna, who lives in Paris and whose photographs appear in all the leading French fashion magazines, is also a devotee of the hot-water-and-lemon before breakfast routine, as are her two friends, Marielle, a beautiful Parisian model, and the young French socialite Laetitia d'Elchingen, daughter of the Duke of Elchingen and a descendant of Napoleon's famous Marshal Ney.

No one knows just how old this beauty treatment is, but it has been recorded that Queen Victoria used it in her younger days and that *she* got it from one of her grandmothers. Victoria drank a glass of hot water and lemon juice not only every morning upon rising but also every night just before she went to bed. (And don't think of her only as she appeared in her old-age pictures! She was attractive and had a pretty complexion when she was young.)

Fashion magazines occasionally divulge the beauty secrets of famous socialites. It is surprising how often these turn out to be old-time recipes: the use of eggs and rum in shampoos; egg-white facial masks; camomile tea as a rinse for the hair after shampooing; fruit juices and vegetables on the face. (Last winter, for example, *Vogue* reported the craze among Italian beauties for cleaning their skins with watermelons.) Among those who have been mentioned, Mrs. Graham Mattison uses almond oil on her face and rinses it with mineral water, having learned from a Parisian dermatologist that mineral waters—like Poland, Evian, etc.—are the best substitute for rain water. And Señora Luis Miguel Dominguin of Madrid (formerly a beautiful Italian movie actress and now wife of the famed bullfighter) has a daily massage with cocoanut and almond oils.

It is somewhat easier to find out the beauty secrets of women in bygone years, as they are a matter of history. Old beauty books, diaries, letters, and chronicles often reveal the tricks used by celebrated charmers to enhance and preserve their good looks.

The famous old-time French beauty Ninon de l'Enclos is the ideal of all lovely ladies who dread the marks of age. Ninon was called "the woman who never grew old" and was said to be still beautiful and still attracting young lovers almost up to the time of her death, at the age of ninety-one. Old chronicles show that she faithfully did exercises to avoid wrinkles in her neck and that she claimed that she owed her youthful skin to her famous beauty mask, which she used night and morning. It was made by boiling one-half pint of fresh milk, one-quarter ounce of lemon juice, and half an ounce of brandy. While still warm it was applied to the face and neck and allowed to dry on the skin.

Marie Antoinette's favorite beauty preparation was buttermilk. She not only drank it every day, but she also put it on her face, neck, shoulders, arms and bosom—sopping it on with a soft linen cloth and letting it dry. She and the ladies of her court believed that it was a wrinkle preventive, and it was credited with being the source of her dazzling complexion.

Since buttermilk as a skin treatment has been popular for many years and still is today, I am willing to believe in its efficacy (and also in Ninon's mask, as milk, lemon juice, and brandy are other old-time favorite cosmetic ingredients), but it is too much to expect me to credit Diane de Poitiers' daily bath in a tub of rain water as the sole reason why she was still a doll at the age of sixty-five. I am sure she must have had other secrets which she refused to reveal.

Another eternally youthful beauty was Queen Elizabeth of Hungary, of whom it has been written that she was so attractive at the age of seventy that an eighteen-year-old boy had a "burning passion" for her. She was said to owe her marvelous looks to the use of an herb tonic which became known, in her honor, as Hungary Water. It was made with:

12 ounces rosemary
1 ounce lemon peel
1 ounce orange peel
1 ounce mint
1 ounce balm
1 pint rose water
1 pint spirits of wine

Mix together and let stand for several weeks. Then strain and use the liquid to rub into the skin after bathing.

Another herb concoction, used by Gaby Delys, a famous French actress and charmer of men, was:

1 ounce mint
1 ounce sage
1 ounce rosemary
1 ounce lavender
1 ounce mixed spices
1 ounce camphor
1 quart white vinegar (Good old vinegar again!)
1 pint alcohol
2 ounces myrrh
2 ounces benzoin

Soak the herbs for two weeks in the vinegar. At the same time soak the camphor in the alcohol. Strain and combine the liquids. Add the myrrh and the benzoin. Sometimes Mlle. Delys used to rub this into her skin and let it dry; at other times, she would add a small amount to her bath water.

The beautiful Spanish Duchess of Alba, adored and painted by Goya as the famous La Maja, both robed and disrobed, used a paste to prevent wrinkles, concocted of the whites of eggs—here we go again!—boiled in rose water. The Spanish version of the recipe would seem to suggest that the eggs were first broken, and the whites then slightly boiled in a small quantity of rose water, just enough to make them soft. Half an ounce of alum and half an ounce of sweet almond oil were then added, and the whole beaten to form a paste.

One of the most beautiful of English queens was Alexandra, wife of Edward VII, and the great-grandmother of Queen Elizabeth II. When Alexandra was still Princess of Wales, her favorite beauty trick was to mix half a pint of milk with the juice of a Portuguese lemon, apply it to her face at night, and wash it off the next morning with soft warm water.

We've all heard of the milk baths of the French actress Anna Held, but an old beauty book revealed a bath that was new to me. It seems that a certain Mme. Tallien, a French beauty of Napoleon's day, attributed her lovely skin to a daily bath prepared with twenty pounds of strawberries and raspberries. The tub was filled with the squashed berries, and Mme. Tallien would hop in and lie there.

Poppaea, Nero's wife, used to take baths in a marble tub filled with strawberry juice or, sometimes, with asses' milk. Isabeau of Bavaria, wife of Charles II, bathed in a liquid made by steeping chickweed in water; Marie Antoinette took baths in which wild thyme, marjoram, and sea salt had been steeped; and Marie Czetwertynoska, mistress of Alexander I of Russia, would only bathe in Malaga wine (which was afterward bottled and sold—well, waste not, want not!).

Other favorite beauty baths, used by court ladies in the eighteenth century, were composed of the water in which veal had been boiled, or water to which had been added melon juice, egg yolks, almond meal, barley or flax seed. The most entertaining baths of all were those taken by Anne Boleyn. An old beauty book reports: "You are doubtless familiar with the degrading sycophancy of the English noblemen who filled their glasses from her bath while she was in it, and drank to her health, with revolting jests." It doesn't say where Henry VIII was at the time, but maybe he joined in the jolly gathering, which all sounds like a forerunner of the celebrated scandal about the party with an Earl Carroll showgirl in a tub of champagne.

The famous French actress Sarah Bernhardt used cucumber juice on her face, while Lola Montez, who cut a wide swath through the hearts of men both in America and in Europe (she counted poets and kings among her numerous famous admirers), used facial masks of honey to enhance her beauty. When Lola's black hair began to show a little gray, she dyed it by boiling equal parts of vinegar, lemon juice and powdered litharge half an hour over a slow fire in a porcelain-lined pot and then combing the mixture through her hair. For a body oil she used:

8 ounces deer or stag fat
6 ounces olive oil
3 ounces white wax

Melt together. Stir four ounces of rose water into a half pint of brandy. Add to the other ingredients and beat.

The dancer Isadora Duncan used to rub coarse salt on her face and body to improve the texture of her skin, but I certainly wouldn't recommend it for delicate skins. However, it is said to be an old-time Russian beauty treatment, and Isadora learned it from her mother. Today, the Countess Czaky, living in London, recommends it as an easy, inexpensive beauty treatment for the body skin. Every year before going to the beach for the summer vacation, she spends a few weeks getting her body in shape. "First, I stand in the bath and rub myself all over with dampened kitchen salt. This preserves the skin against aging and makes it glow all over. Then, into my bath water—not too hot—I put three tablespoons of olive oil. It stays on the top of the water so that when I lie down in the tub I can pick up handfuls of the oil. I massage my body with it for five or ten minutes *under the warm water.*"

She claims it makes the skin smooth and elastic and supple. So perhaps Isadora knew what she was doing after all.

Some of these secrets of famous women of the past could be adapted for use today, although not, of course, to the extent of filling your bathtub with twenty pounds of crushed berries. The berries may be wonderful for your skin, but it's hardly a practical idea for every day in the week. On the other hand, something like buttermilk is easy to obtain and use.

The fact that it was used long ago by Marie Antoinette doesn't mean that it isn't just as good today. Women's skins haven't changed since then—and neither has buttermilk.

This recipe for a dentifrice was used by Queen Victoria and her ladies-in-waiting:

> 1 quart rainwater
> juice of one lemon
> 6 ounces burnt alum
> 6 ounces salt

Boil one minute. Strain into a bottle. Use it to brush the teeth three times a day.

Here is a skin ointment originally made for Mary, Queen of Scots, in 1569 and later copied by Queen Victoria in her scrapbook and used by her and by her ladies-in-waiting:

> 4 parts oil of almonds
> 4 parts whale oil
> 4 ounces red rose water

Mix together with a silver spoon to make a smooth paste, and apply to skin.

Another skin ointment thought to have been used by Mary, Queen of Scots, was:

> 1-1/2 parts olive oil
> 1 part whale oil (or lard)
> 1 part virgin wax
> 1 part camphor
> 2 parts honey

Mix in a silver dish and then heat in a pan of hot water, stirring until dissolved. Remove from hot water and keep stirring until cold.

You will notice that both of these recipes contain the old stand-bys—almond oil, olive oil, lard, camphor, honey, rose water. It stands to reason that the same ingredients wouldn't have been used by so many women in different centuries if they weren't recognizably beneficial.

The following sixteenth century recipe was a cure for blisters and flea bites:

2 ounces oil of scorpions
2 ounces hedgehog grease
2 ounces badger grease
2 ounces bear grease
1/2 pint olive oil

Mix all together, spread on a linen cloth, and apply to spot. First, of course, you have to catch your scorpions, hedgehog, bear, and badger!

This ointment, which was doubtless very effective in its day, was also used at the court of Mary, Queen of Scots, although the old beauty book in which I read it did not specify whether it was used for the royal flea bites or just the common courtier variety.

Throughout history, queens have been just as interested in beauty preparations as their more humble sisters, and often more so, especially the giddier ones like Anne Boleyn, Mary Queen of Scots, and Marie Antoinette. Even if they all lost their pretty heads in the end, they took good care of them while they still had them.

16

Do-It-Yourself Creams

The do-it-yourself urge has spread widely in the past years, symbolic, perhaps, of a growing discontent with our packaged civilization which has robbed us of one of the greatest satisfactions known to mankind—that of creating something with our own hands.

Thus we find many people of wealth, who certainly could afford to buy anything they liked ready-made or to have it made for them, who instead prefer to make these things themselves, just for the joy of doing it. I know several people who have started to bake bread at home, among them one man, president of a large investment firm, who happily makes his own loaves of coarse wheat bread every summer after grinding the wheat by hand, and is proud as can be of himself.

There is no reason why you cannot make your own cosmetics, and many women do. Naturally, this is easier if you live in a house with a good-sized kitchen than it is in a city apartment. However, I know a

137

woman who makes her own soap, with lye and fats, although she lives in a small apartment in an expensive residential hotel on New York's fashionable Upper East Side. It's her hobby, and she enjoys it.

Another friend of mine has made her own cold cream for years in a Greenwich Village apartment with a little kitchenette. She says she does it because she can put in exactly the ingredients which she knows from experience are best for her individual skin. That, of course, is one of the best reasons. When you make your own cold cream, you know what's in it. Furthermore, you can put in it just what you want and need. Another reason is that it's a great deal cheaper than buying it in a store. You can use the purest and most luxurious ingredients for a tiny fraction of what it would cost you to buy a similar ready-made cream. Finally, the third reason is that a great many women thoroughly enjoy this kind of puttering around, mixing up different batches of ingredients.

Although some of the ingredients in the older recipes may not be kept in stock by your druggist, most of them are, or at least most of them can be ordered by a drugstore from a wholesale house. But the ingredients haven't varied too much, really, since the first cold cream on record—that is, cold cream as we know it today—was compounded by Galen, a physician of Asia Minor and Rome, who lived from 130 to 200 A.D. and wrote a whole scientific textbook on cosmetics.

Here are some of the best recipes:

STRAWBERRY CREAM

    1/2 ounce white wax
    1/2 ounce spermaceti
    2-1/2 ounces sweet almond oil
    3/4 ounce strawberry juice
    3 drops benzion

Take large fresh berries. Wash and drain thoroughly. Mash them and strain the juice through a piece of muslin or cheese cloth. Heat the white wax, spermaceti and oil of almonds in a double boiler. Remove from the fire and add the strawberry juice very quickly. Beat briskly till fluffy. Add the three drops of benzoin just as the mixture begins to cool and mix it in well. Put in a jar and keep in the icebox, at least till it hardens enough. This quantity will make enough to fill a three-ounce jar. Apply every night.

Of course, any of these recipes may be more beneficial to some skins than to others—here again, you are the only one who can decide what is best for your own skin.

ORANGE FLOWER SKIN FOOD

1/2 ounce spermaceti
1/2 ounce white wax
2 ounces sweet almond oil
1 ounce lanolin
1 ounce cocoanut oil
3 drops tincture of benzoin
1 ounce orange flower water

Melt the first five ingredients in a double boiler (or porcelain pot over very low gentle heat). Remove from the fire and add the benzoin and the orange flower water, beating with an egg beater till fluffy. (You can use an electric beater in these recipes. They didn't have them in the days when the recipes were first used, but it should certainly make less work today.) Beat until cold. This recipe will make five ounces of cream. It is a cream which is quickly absorbed by the skin, without being greasy, and is said to help obliterate lines and prevent wrinkles.

CLOVER CREAM

1 ounce spermaceti
1 ounce white wax
5 ounces sweet almond oil

                    1-3/5 ounces rose water
                       20 grains powdered borax
                        5 drops essence of clover

Dissolve the borax in the rose water and add the
clover essence. Melt the wax, spermaceti and almond
oil, using a porcelain pot or double boiler. (Try not
to use any tin or metal utensils in making creams.)
When melted, remove from heat and add the rose
water with the borax and clover in it. Beat until cold
and firm. This recipe provides about eight ounces of
cream, so maybe you should only make half of it at
first in order to try it.

CAMPHOR COLD CREAM

                    1/2 ounce spermaceti
                    1/2 ounce white wax
                 3-1/4 ounces oil of sweet almonds
                    1/4 ounce camphor
                 1-1/2 ounces distilled water
                     15 grains borax
                      4 drops oil of rose geranium

Melt the wax and spermaceti together. Add the almond oil. Stir. Then add the camphor. (If you use
lump camphor, break into small pieces before adding
and stir until dissolved.) Dissolve the borax in the
distilled water and add to the rest. Stir until it is
well mixed and beginning to thicken. Remove from
fire and stir until it begins to cool. Add the rose
geranium oil. Continue to beat until cold.

VIOLET COLD CREAM

                      1 ounce white wax
                      1 ounce spermaceti
                      5 ounces sweet almond oil
                 1-1/2 ounces rose water
                     10 grains borax
                    1/2 teaspoon essence of violets

Cut the wax and spermaceti into fine shavings and melt together. When melted, add the almond oil and heat, but do not let it boil. Remove from fire and quickly pour in the rose water, in which you have previously dissolved the borax. Beat briskly. When the mixture begins to thicken, add the essence of violets and stir in. When nearly cold, put in little jars. This cream is effective when used at night after you have washed your face with warm water and soap.

COCOA BUTTER CREAM

123 grains white wax
123 grains spermaceti
464 grains sweet almond oil
464 grains cocoa butter

(I don't know why this particular recipe is given in grains instead of in ounces, like the others, but the woman who gave it to me had it written down that way in her family Bible, along with births, deaths, marriages, and other important records. I'm sure your druggist can translate it into ounces for you or advise you how to do it.)

Mix all together in a double boiler, stirring with a silver spoon. When melted and mixed, let it cool.

CUCUMBER CREAM

1 pound cucumbers, peeled
1 pound melon pulp
1 pound pure white lard
1/2 pint milk

Cut the cucumber and melon into small pieces. Add the lard and milk and heat in a double boiler for ten hours without letting boil. Strain through a cloth over a sieve, into a bowl. Let drip and congeal. Then keep in small jars. (I don't suppose you have to put all these creams in "small jars." I imagine you could keep them any way you like as long as it's not in metal containers, which seem to be bad for the oils.) I like the way this cream sounds.

One of the most highly recommended of the homemade creams, although I have never tried it, is the one known to our grandmothers as Crème Marquise. This is the way to make it:

CREME MARQUISE

1/4 ounce white wax
2-1/2 ounces spermaceti
1-1/2 ounces oil of sweet almonds
1-1/2 ounces rose water
1 drop attar of roses

Shave the wax and spermaceti and melt. Add the almond oil and heat gently, but do not let boil. Remove from the fire and add the rose water, to which the perfume has been added. Beat until creamy, but stop beating before it gets really hard.

Because Crème Marquise is a whiter, harder preparation than some of the others, it is more difficult to make. It will crumble if made carelessly—or if fussed over too much. This cream is easier:

1/2 ounce white wax
1 ounce spermaceti
1 pint almond oil
1-1/2 ounces glycerine
6 drops attar of roses

Mix the wax, spermaceti and almond oil together over low heat till melted; add the glycerine just before removing from the fire and the rose drops after it has cooled. Stir till nearly cold, using a silver spoon.

Don't worry if your cream doesn't harden. You can use it as a lotion. There's no reason why it won't work just as well since the ingredients are the same, and there's no law that says they aren't as good in liquid form as in solid. And don't be discouraged if you make a mess of it all the first time. Your first cake isn't always a howling success either!

If you just want to try making a little of one cream to see how it turns out, I don't see why you couldn't do it without getting a lot of special equipment. Ordinarily, you're supposed to have a non-metal double boiler, a liquid measure (measuring cup or graduate), bone or glass or silver spoons, a glass funnel (although you could use china or porcelain), cheese cloth for straining, a mortar and pestle (you can buy cheap wooden ones nowadays), filtering paper, which can be purchased at a druggist's or sometimes at coffee shops, and small scales such as a pharmacist uses. It is preferable not to use any tin or metal. Also, because perfect cleanliness is essential, you are not supposed to use utensils which have been used for cooking foods, although I suppose in a pinch these could be scoured clean and then boiled. Your pharmacist can give you some tips on mixing the ingredients, or perhaps he'll do it for you.

Personally, I prefer recipes which contain lanolin instead of the white wax. Some cleansing lotions do not contain the wax or the spermaceti. One of the best—and the easiest to make—is the fabulous anti-wrinkle cream for which I gave you the recipe in Chapter 13. It used to be used especially for crows' feet, but you don't have to wait until you start getting them. As I said before, it is fine for the face, neck, elbows, hands and even the feet.

Another very old and celebrated recipe, dating back as far as the seventeenth century, is the following cleansing lotion:

VIRGINAL MILK

1 pint rose water, orange flower water, or elderflower water

1/2 ounce simple tincture of benzoin
10 drops tincture of myrrh
10 drops glycerine

Put the rose water (or whichever one you use) in a bowl, and stir in, drop by drop, with a glass or porcelain spoon, the benzoin, then the myrrh, then the glycerine. (If you don't like glycerine, just omit it from the recipe.) This is supposed to be good for cleansing the skin of all dirt and make-up.

PERFUMED CLEANSING LOTION

4 ounces oil of sweet almonds
1 ounce lanolin
1 ounce white petroleum jelly
10 drops violet extract

Melt the fats over a low fire or in double boiler. Remove from fire and beat until cool, adding the perfume drop by drop. Any perfume may be used, such as extract of jasmine, or attar of roses, or whatever scent you prefer.

Here is the recipe for Crème Simon, a famous old-time cream made without the wax. It sounds very nourishing as a skin food.

CREME SIMON

2 ounces cocoa butter
2 ounces lanolin
2 ounces glycerine
2-1/2 ounces rose water
1-1/2 ounces elderflower water

Omit the glycerine if your skin doesn't react well to it.

You know, the joy of making your own creams and lotions is that you don't have to follow any of these recipes at all. You can make up your own, using lanolin, castor oil, almond oil, whatever you want, and perfuming it with your favorite scent. In this way, you can make the cream best suited to your own skin, and who knows—you may just happen to invent a real miracle cream!

17

Speaking Frankly

I have read, in my day, some long-winded and monumentally boring books on beauty and charm in which I had to plough through pages of platitudes in order to find the few nuggets of practical advice.

In this book I have tried as much as possible to avoid that sort of thing. I have avoided the scientific jargon about proteins and vitamins because my primary interest is not in *why* honey or oatmeal or raw eggs improve my skin. What I care about is the fact that they do. If I am going to put something on my face—which, after all, is the only one I have—all I want to know is (a) will it really benefit it and (b) in what way?

I have leaned over backward to be careful and to emphasize that not all preparations are equally beneficial to all women. Even when repeating recipes which in old beauty books were prefaced by the reassurance, "This is harmless," I have added a word of caution. I know that the basic oils, grains, fruit and vegetable juices, and other foods that form the ingredients of most of the recipes are absolutely harmless. I know what has worked for me and for other women. In those cases where I don't know for sure, I have said so.

I have pointed out that nothing is going to perform any magical change overnight. If the expensive commercial products really worked as miraculously as their advertisements claim, it stands to reason that all the female employees and the other women connected with the various companies that get them out would be eternally youthful beauties. They aren't.

Any of the treatments have to be kept up regularly for a reasonable length of time in order to give them a fair chance to work. In some cases, you can see actual improvement within one month; in others, it may take as long as six months. Too many women get bored with their treatments and abandon them in the early stages, whereas they are more apt to keep on using a commercial product in order to get their money's worth. On the other hand, this works in another way, too. If you find you don't like, say, lemon juice or vinegar, all you have lost is a few pennies, but if you have spent five or ten dollars for a jar of stuff in a store you feel you have to use it up even if you hate it. One of the advantages, therefore, of these old-time treatments is that you can feel perfectly free to experiment without its costing a lot.

Naturally, some of the old-fashioned treatments take more time and trouble than others, and it isn't necessary to use them today. We can simplify a lot of them. In olden times the menfolk went out and shot the bear or killed the sheep, and the womenfolk boiled the meat on the stove for hours and hours to render the fat and thus get the bear's grease or the mutton tallow for their cosmetic. Today, it is more practical to go to the drugstore and buy pure lanolin. The basic idea, however, is the same. The carcasses of the sheep are boiled to extract the fat, only the work is done in a factory instead of on the kitchen stove.

The one cosmetic area in which we have made the most notable improvement is in the manufacture of make-up. Women didn't use it as much as we do now, and those few who did want to had a pretty tough time of it. One old beauty book says, "Let

every woman understand that paint can do nothing
for the mouth and lips. The advantage gained by the
artificial red is a thousand times more than lost by
the sure destruction of that delicate charm associated
with the idea of 'nature's dewy lip.' There can be no
dew on a painted lip. And there is no man who does
not shrink back with disgust from the idea of kissing
a pair of painted lips."

Despite this harsh warning, a few rash women did
venture to gild the lily, but the means at their dis-
posal were primitive. One device was to pound
cooked beets in a mortar and then press the pulp
through a fine sieve, add alcohol to the resulting
juice, and then apply to the lips and cheeks with
absorbent cotton.

Rouge was sold in the form of "Spanish wool" and
"Spanish papers." These were, as the names indicate,
wool and paper made in Spain and impregnated with
red dyes from cochineal (obtained from the dried
bodies of insects). They were dampened with water
and then rubbed on the cheeks and lips.

When my grandmother was a girl, there was a woman in her village who used to soak a red silk artificial
rose in a saucer of water and then use the liquid to
tint her cheeks and lips. It was quite a scandal in the
community.

Powder was plain talcum powder, made from chalk
or from rice powder imported from the Orient.
There were only two shades: dead white and pink
made by dyeing it with cochineal. An old recipe for
the talc powder went as follows:

"Take a piece of Briancon chalk. Choose it of a
pearl gray color, and rasp it gently with a piece of
dogskin. After this, sift it through a sieve of very
fine silk, and put this powder into a pint of very good
distilled vinegar, in which leave it for a fortnight.
Shake the bottle every day except the last, on which
it must not be disturbed. Pour off the vinegar so as
to leave the chalk behind in the bottle, into which
pour clean water that has been distilled and filtered.

Throw the whole into a clean pan, and stir the water well with a wooden spatula. Let the powder settle again to the bottom. Then pour the water gently off, and wash the powder six or seven times, taking care always to use filtered or distilled water. When the powder is soft and white as you wish, dry it in a place where it is not exposed to the dust. Sift it through a silken sieve, which will make it still finer. It is used by dipping the finger, or a hare's foot, in cold cream, and putting upon it a touch of the powder, then applying to the face. It will not be removed even by perspiration."

Small wonder that our great-grandmothers generally preferred to go around with shiny faces rather than work their way laboriously through all that rigmarole!

The very best powder of all was made by grinding real pearls and was, naturally, very expensive. An early nineteenth century beauty book advises that "the best way to obtain this pearl powder is to commission some friend who may be going to China to purchase it."

There is really nothing new under the sun; it's just that mass manufacture has replaced the homemade product and, in some instances, improved it. Women in Minoan Crete nearly four thousand years ago used to wear tight metal belts to make their waists look small. Today, we can buy waist cinchers, only slightly less uncomfortable. False bosoms made of India rubber were popular in the nineteenth century. A news item in the Hartford, Connecticut, *Times* in 1880 reported that a man had been arrested for stealing "a palpitating bosom" from a store in that city. That particular type of false bosom was called a "plumer" and was used, according to an old book, "for artificially rounding out the female bust and palpitating with it." Later on, other types of artificial bosoms were constructed of braided wire. Even the early Christians in ancient Rome used lotions and oils that were supposed to develop the bust: concoctions of myrrh and olive oil and cocoa butter. And in the eighteenth century, young French girls who were "backward," a euphemism of the day for flat-chested, used to sleep with poultices of bread and sage tea on their breasts, although I strongly doubt if that ever did them much good.

These historical items are entertaining to read about, but they play only a minor role in this book. The purpose of the book has been to give you the practical, simple, old-time home beauty secrets that you yourself can use advantageously today. I know that at least three or four of them have been worth more to me than all the time and money I have spent in beauty parlors.

A year ago, after I had had the flu, I discovered to my horror that I had dandruff and that, worse, my hair was falling out. Every time I combed it, it came out literally in handfuls. I happened to be in a small European community where there were no hairdressing salons. In desperation I remembered the old-time remedies. First I rubbed my scalp with equal parts of vinegar and water. The next day I massaged it with warm olive oil, and the following day I shampooed it with castile soap. Then I started brushing it one hundred strokes a day until the next week, when I repeated the whole process. After the first treatment alone, there was a definite decrease in the amount of hair that came out. After the second treatment, only a few hairs came out on my brush—the average, normal amount. After the third treatment, not a hair came out. As for the dandruff, it disappeared after the first shampoo, but in four or five days it started to reappear—although nothing like the snowstorm it had been before. After the second week's shampoo, it disappeared and never came back. I couldn't have been more surprised. Frankly, I had forgotten just how effective some of these old-time treatments really are.

This holds true even for some of the sillier-sounding ones. Why should we pooh-pooh them as ridiculous and then go out and pay a lot of money for something advertised as containing mink oil or turtle oil or the afterbirth of cows? The cosmetic manufacturers think enough of animal oils and vegetable and fruit juices to use them in their expensive preparations. Think this over for a minute, and then don't let anyone laugh you out of trying at least a few of these old-fashioned treatments. Sure, you may feel silly at first putting eggs and other food on your face, but what's silly about it when they really work? And the fabulous fact is that they do!

Tables of Weights and Measures

APOTHECARIES' WEIGHTS

(use apothecary scales)

60 grains	= 1 dram
8 drams	= 1 ounce
12 ounces	= 1 pound
15-1/2 grains	= 1 gram

APOTHECARIES' LIQUID MEASURES

60 minims or drops	= 1 liquid dram
8 liquid drams	= 1 liquid ounce
16 liquid ounces	= 1 liquid pint
1-1/3 drams	= 1 common teaspoon
3 teaspoons	= 1 tablespoon

Index

155

156

159